The Joy of
Sensual
MASSAGE

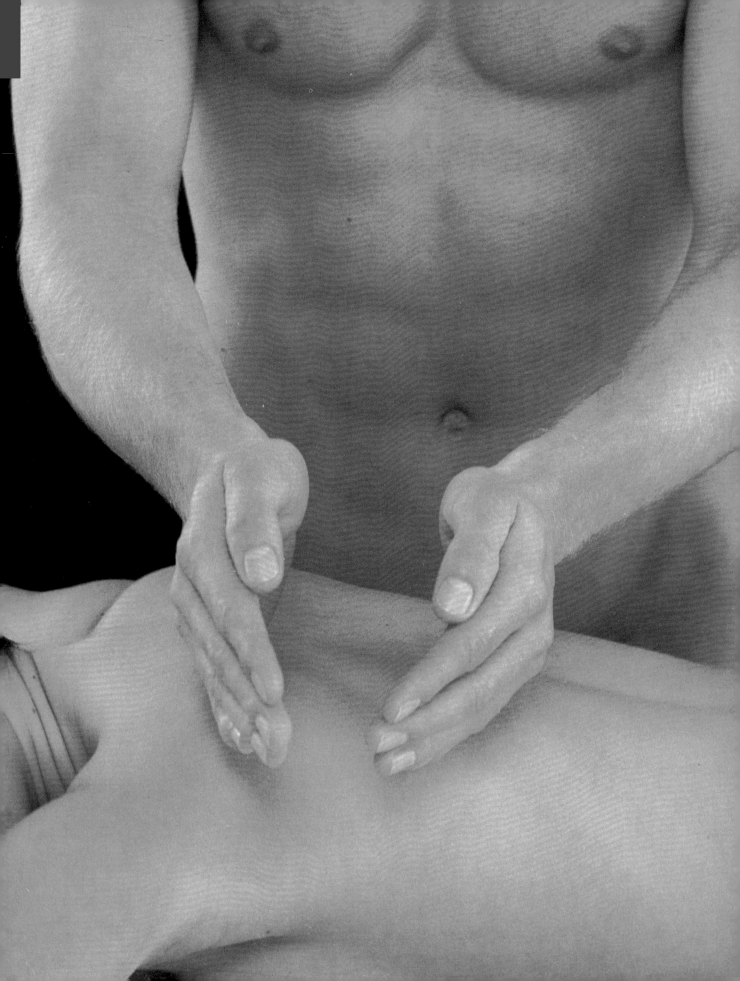

The Joy of
Sensual
MASSAGE

Roger W. Hicks & Victoria Day

WARD LOCK

A WARD LOCK BOOK

First published in the UK 1994 by Ward Lock,
Villiers House, 41/47 Strand, LONDON, WC2N 5JE

A Cassell Imprint

Copyright © 1994
Text: Roger W.Hicks and Victoria Day
Illustrations: Ward Lock

Distributed in the United States by Sterling Publishing Co., Inc.
387 Park Avenue South, New York, NY 10016-8810

Distributed in Australia by Capricorn Link (Australia) Pty Ltd.
2/13 Carrington Road, Castle Hill NSW 2154

A British Library Cataloguing in Publication Data block for this book may be obtained from the British Library.

ISBN 0 7063 7293 X
Paperback ISBN 0 7063 7332 4 (USA only)

Designed by Richard Carr
Page Make-up and Typesetting by Associated Print Production Ltd.
Printed and bound in Spain by Cronion S.A., Barcelona

CONTENTS

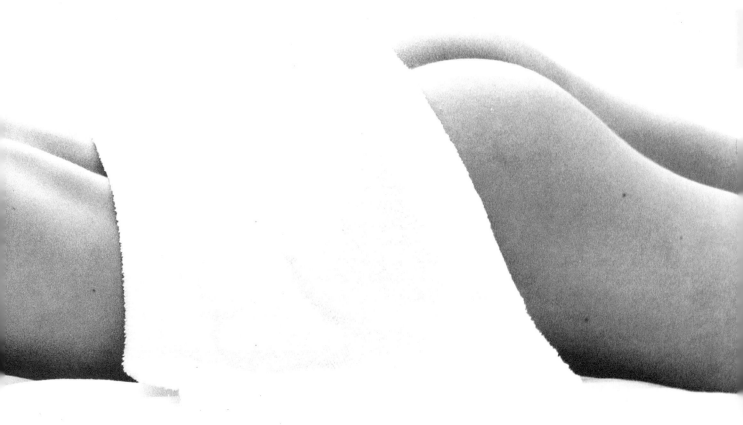

The Power of MASSAGE

I F THERE IS ONE WORD which sums up all that sensual massage should be, it is languor. Languor is (or can be) that delicious sense of relaxation and well-being which is akin to tiredness; a sense that the cares of the world are far away or unimportant, and that all that matters is the pleasurable moment. It is a dreamy, floating feeling that can be achieved without drugs or alcohol; a dimension in which you can fall asleep, make love, or just cuddle.

Although sensual massage is generally seen as something between lovers, it need not be so; nor need it end in sexual encounters. Sensual massage is a wonderful method of bonding between mothers and babies, or fathers and babies for that matter. Old friends can massage one another, too, though the areas they massage will necessarily be circumscribed: a head and neck massage, or a foot massage, will normally be all that is socially acceptable. If the friends are of the same sex, even those innocent sensualities may be proscribed by society.

The sad truth is that the various cultures of Europe and North America are for the most part extraordinarily puritanical when it comes to touch. In much of Asia, touch plays a far greater part in everyday life. In India or in Thailand, for example, it is quite common to see two men holding hands as they converse. This is hard for a Westerner to accept at first, though after a while, it begins to make a lot of sense: it is a way of saying 'I am pleased to see you and to be with you, and I am giving you my undivided attention.' It is much more immediate and genuine than the handshakes of the West, or the formal peck on the cheek, which are bestowed whether we like someone or not. Holding someone's hand when you talk to them, however, is something you only do with a friend.

Because touching is so circumscribed and formalized in Western society, massage is doubly important. Not only is it enjoyable in its own sense: it also represents a way of breaking down the barriers which divide us from one another. Even lovers may be unsure of how to touch one another, except perhaps at the most basic and instinctive

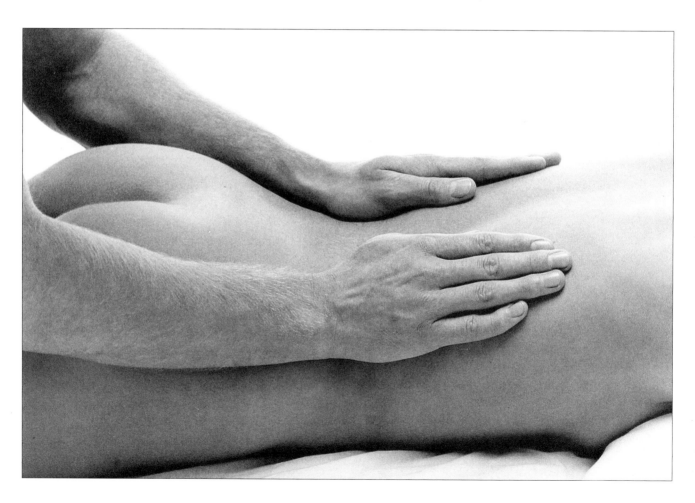

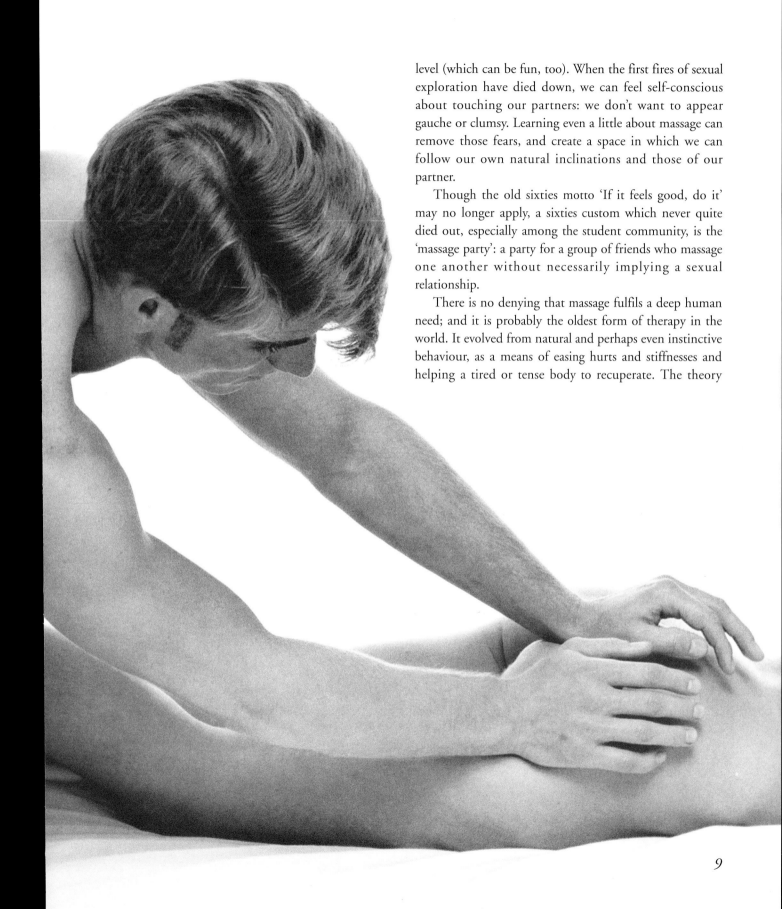

level (which can be fun, too). When the first fires of sexual exploration have died down, we can feel self-conscious about touching our partners: we don't want to appear gauche or clumsy. Learning even a little about massage can remove those fears, and create a space in which we can follow our own natural inclinations and those of our partner.

Though the old sixties motto 'If it feels good, do it' may no longer apply, a sixties custom which never quite died out, especially among the student community, is the 'massage party': a party for a group of friends who massage one another without necessarily implying a sexual relationship.

There is no denying that massage fulfils a deep human need; and it is probably the oldest form of therapy in the world. It evolved from natural and perhaps even instinctive behaviour, as a means of easing hurts and stiffnesses and helping a tired or tense body to recuperate. The theory

which grew up around it was sometimes valuable, and sometimes valueless, but the practice was less open to over-elaboration and fantasy. A number of very simple and effective techniques can be garnered from all the countless schools and sub-schools of massage, and by putting them into practice, you can greatly increase the benefits of massage for both parties.

This is why, in these pages, we have concentrated very much on the practical aspects of massage. The theory has its place, perhaps, for advanced students of different schools of massage, but for sensual massage, there is absolutely no need to learn any of this.

Although we are avowed pragmatists who believe that theory is much overrated in comparison with practice, we still do harbour some feelings about massage which border on mysticism. The most important of these is massage as communication. Anthropologists estimate that anything up to ninety per cent of everyday human communication is non-verbal, though obviously this figure will vary widely, and some anthropologists place it as low as sixty per cent, spread across a typical day. For example, cashing a cheque

at a bank can be accomplished with very little non-verbal communication, while if you met the same bank clerk at a party the same night and one of you found the other attractive, verbal communication might count for very little next to body language, facial expression, tone of voice, the distance you stand apart, the brightness of your eyes and even the level of pheromones, among a dozen other non-verbal signals.

On the most mystical level, it sometimes seems almost as if messages, and what the ancients called 'virtue', can flow through touch: remember the biblical story of the woman who touched the hem of Jesus's robe and was healed. Whether there is any objective reality to this phenomenon is irrelevant, because what we are dealing with is human perception. If we think that we are communicating through touch, or if we feel that we are, then we are doing so. Or maybe there is no mysticism here at all: maybe a touch conveys 'I am here, I am with you', the most basic reassurance that human beings can give to one another. In sensual massage, that reassurance is extended to the message 'I care about you'.

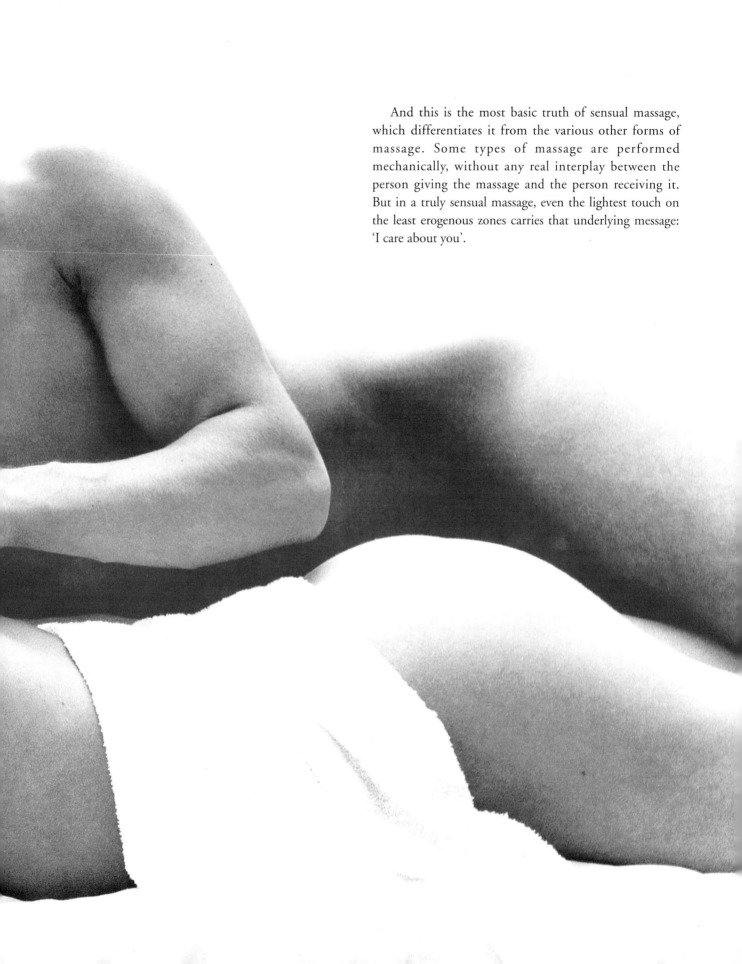

And this is the most basic truth of sensual massage, which differentiates it from the various other forms of massage. Some types of massage are performed mechanically, without any real interplay between the person giving the massage and the person receiving it. But in a truly sensual massage, even the lightest touch on the least erogenous zones carries that underlying message: 'I care about you'.

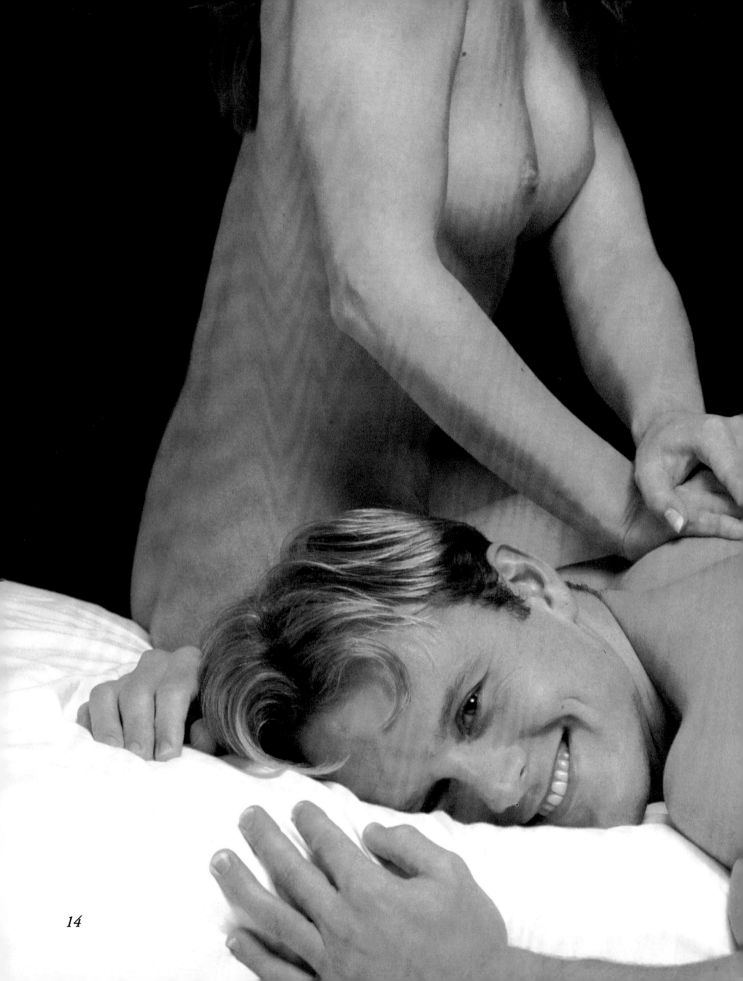

Before You *START*

M ASSAGE BY ITS very essence is sensual. The effect of touch can be stimulating, relaxing, or enjoyable, or it can be all three; but only if both parties want it to be so. You cannot inflict massage, as if upon a victim; you have to share it willingly.

Viewed scientifically, massage works by relaxing and refreshing tired or knotted muscles; by stimulating the nerve endings in the superficial layers of the skin; by increasing the blood circulation in the capillaries; by improving deep circulation, both of the blood and of lymph; and by stimulating the production of endorphins, which are the brain's own natural opiates.

15

Relaxing muscles is one of the most familiar forms of massage, and one that is often done without any formal knowledge of massage techniques. Everyone must have had the experience of gentle fingers finding the 'knot' in a stiff muscle, then of the blessed sense of release, after a few seconds' pain, as it is massaged back into flexibility.

The stimulation of the nerve endings is important because it makes you more alive, more aware of your body and of your self. In the modern jargon, it 'centres' you.

The increase in capillary circulation has many effects. The most immediate and obvious of these is that the skin begins to feel warm and relaxed, because of the increased blood flow. Improved blood supply gives healthier, more elastic and younger-looking skin. Skin that is regularly massaged is better able to repair minor damage such as grazes and bites.

Together with the increase in deep circulation, improved capillary flow means that toxins are more rapidly and effectively removed from the skin and from other organs, and are therefore excreted sooner. There may be something in the old expression 'purifying the blood' after all.

Endorphins are the subject of an increasing number of studies. They are known to ease pain, aid relaxation, and create an overall feeling of well-being which can even

For massage to feel good your hands and fingers should not be held tight or rigid. Squeezing a rubber ball aids relaxation and flexibility in the fingers.

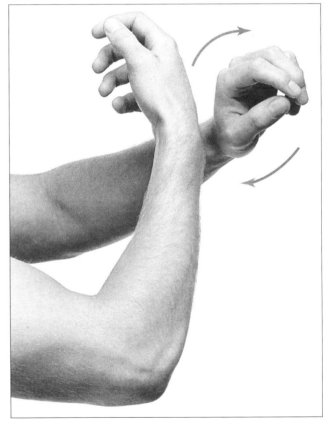

Place the sides of your hands together at the wrists so that the hands are crossed and the palms are facing outwards – rotate around each other to help suppleness.

approach euphoria. Neither the chemistry nor the precise mechanism of action of endorphins is fully understood, but there is no doubt that they exist, and there is equally little doubt that their production is stimulated by massage.

There is however more to massage than quantifiable scientific benefits. For a start, the person who is being massaged usually feels pampered and soothed, yet paradoxically refreshed and invigorated.

Massage can also be reassuring, building self-confidence. This may be a side-effect of the endorphins, but equally, it may well be the result of interacting with another person, the masseur or masseuse, and of receiving their undivided attention. This is a powerful affirmation of self-worth.

Nor are the benefits of massage confined to the person who is being massaged. The masseur or masseuse can also feel invigorated and refreshed: in the right circumstances, it should be as enjoyable to give a massage as to receive one. This is partly for the reasons given above — massage is a form of exercise, after all — and partly a result of sharing something which is very hard to describe. Call it empathy, or energy, or physical pleasure; it is all of these, and more. It really is rather mystical.

This is why massage can be particularly well suited to people who are already close to one another. It can bring the kind of benefits listed above to old friends (or just good friends), and it can bring parents and children closer together; but for couples and lovers, massage can be still more.

With the right person, massage can be a means of coming closer and understanding one another better. As described in the Introduction, it is a means of communication without words; a kind of communication which may not be precise, but which is enormously powerful and unmistakable in both form and content. McLuhan's phrase can for once be quoted accurately: 'The medium is the massage.'

Massage is the opposite, in fact, of a 'vicious circle' or 'vicious spiral' — a benevolent circle, perhaps. It builds on the regard, trust and intimacy which two people share, so that from the smallest seed of intent there can grow an enormous tree of happiness, fulfilment, call it what you will.

The frame of mind that you need for sensual massage is one of openness, and of awareness both of yourself and of your partner.

You need to ask yourself where the tensions are in your body. As massage becomes more and more a part of your world picture, this will become increasingly automatic, but initially, it may require a little thought. For example, it may be that you habitually sit in a chair (or the driving seat of a car) which is uncomfortable, but not so bad that you really notice. It is just that at the end of a long day, or a long journey, you feel stiff, tight and 'headachey'. You may have grown resigned to this; there is, you may feel, nothing you can do about it.

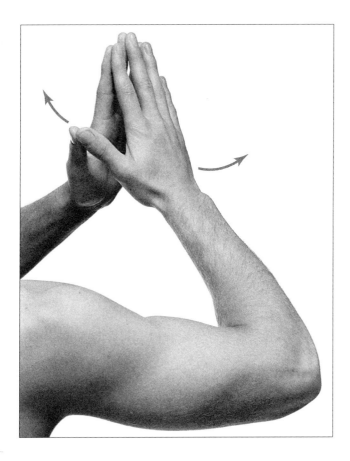

For further flexibility, hold your hands together as if praying, elbows out to the side. Press your fingers together like a spring several times.

Wrong. There is. It is called massage. In fact, many people do an almost instinctive massage on their partners' necks and shoulders, when one or both get home after a day at work. Although these very simple massages can be effective, enjoyable, and sensuous, a 'proper' massage using the correct techniques will be even better. Not least, the person who is giving the massage will be able to do it for longer, because his or her hands will not grow tired so quickly, nor will backache intervene.

But it is only by being aware of your own body, that you can begin to be aware of someone else's. Unless you know what a particular hurt feels like, and how you would like to have it soothed, you really cannot begin to try to help someone else. You will not necessarily be able to transfer your own experience without modification, but unless you have some experience to start with, you cannot do anything. Of course, we all have some experience to start with — we are born with it — but some people are very much more aware than others. In particular, we have probably all had the experience of being irritated by a specific touch which we know was intended by the other party to be pleasurable for us.

As you and your partner become more accustomed to giving and receiving massage, you will inevitably become more and more aware of one another's bodies: what feels good, what does not, what may not feel good as it is being done but feels good when it is finished, and so forth. You will also learn how to use different techniques to relax your partner, or to invigorate them. People's responses vary, and something which one person finds only mildly stimulating or relaxing may have a much more marked effect on another. You and your partner may not respond in the same way, but learning this is part of the fun.

Also, you are likely to find that massage becomes a part of your everyday life, instead of something new and exotic. This does not mean that it becomes dull or boring; rather the reverse. It means that you will continue to discover new pleasures, and that massage becomes more spontaneous and natural. At first, you may have to plan a massage session, as described in Chapter 4, but after a while, you will find that you have all that you need, both physically and mentally, and that massage becomes totally integrated into the way you live.

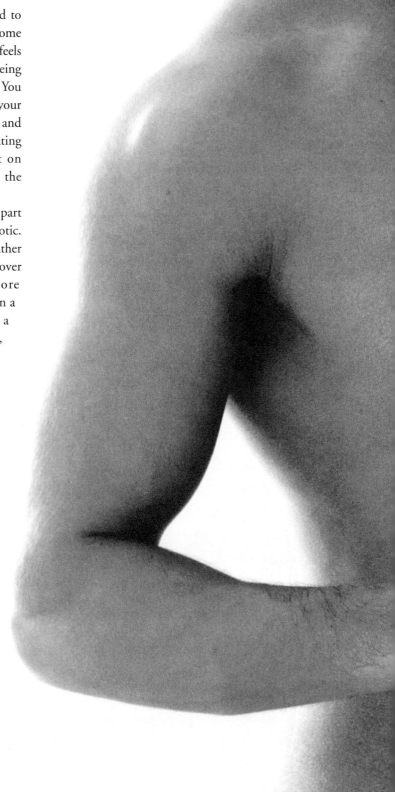

CHAPTER 2

Massage and RELATED SKILLS

A S WE HAVE already said, the simplest forms of massage are not something you learn: they are something you do instinctively. A pair of shy teenagers holding hands; a mother cradling her baby; two lovers in a warm embrace; all are examples of the power and importance of touch. Stroking a tired limb or an aching forehead, or trying to work the stiffness out of a partner's neck or feet, are closer to formal techniques of massage, and indeed they are the origins of it; but they are something which brings relief whether or not you have been trained , just from the reassurance of contact.

A neck and shoulders massage, with the recipient sitting in a chair, must be one of the most familiar and everyday types of massage. You may find it easier if your partner sits facing the 'wrong way' on the chair, with his or her arms resting on the back. You may also find it more comfortable to sit down yourself, perhaps on a stool. Otherwise, your back can get tired quite quickly as you are giving the massage.

Massaging the large, strong muscles between the neck and the shoulders is one of the most immediately relaxing and effective techniques that you can possibly learn. With your hands straddling your partner's shoulders, fingers at the front, thumbs resting on the muscles, you gently probe with the thumbs for knots of tension and soothe them away. Using the pads of your thumbs is much more soothing and effective than digging in with the tips! Meanwhile, a gentle squeezing (not digging) motion with the fingers complements the movement of the thumbs.

A simple neck and shoulders massage with someone sitting in a chair is almost completely instinctive, and would not normally make any use of massage oils. Somewhat less obvious is the idea of supporting your partner's head with one hand, and massaging the back of the neck with the other. Use of the hand to support the forehead makes the neck massage much more effective.

Consider extending a neck and shoulders massage by massaging the upper back. Begin with your hands in the small of the back, and slowly stroke upwards on either side of the spine. When you reach the top of the shoulder-blades, turn your hands so that the fingers point outwards, and go gently downwards, slightly outside the path you followed before. Repeat this several times, stroking with each hand alternately. To finish off, gently stroke down the sides of the spine from the nape of the neck to just above the small of the back. At the very end, use the tips of your fingers for a delicate feathering stroke in the same area.

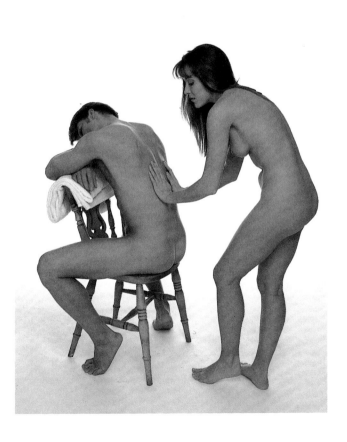

The development of massage from these simple, instinctive techniques has been a long path, and it is not hard to imagine how it happened. In any family, any tribe, any king's court, there would have been some people who were better at the beginnings of massage than others. They would try to pass on their skills, formally or informally, with or without an added freight of theory. They were often highly regarded: in ancient Rome, masseurs were as highly respected as physicians.

Whole schools of massage must have risen and fallen across the centuries, and the ones which remain today are not just an example of the survival of the fittest. Often, the personality of the teachers has been as important as what they taught. It also happens that traditional schools from other cultures are periodically 'discovered' and adopted in the West. There is nothing new about this: the Romans regarded the Greeks as the font of all wisdom, while the Greeks looked to the ancient Egyptians.

One thing which almost all schools of massage have in common, and which is not necessarily a part of 'instinctive' massage, is the use of oils. Used sparingly — not so thickly that the skin becomes oily and slippery — they allow the hands to move smoothly and without dragging, as well as greatly reducing the risk of digging in or pinching uncomfortably. Because they lubricate the skin, they make it more flexible and allow you to massage more deeply. Massage oils (or massage 'media') are equally important on both dry skin and oily skin: they help to reduce irritation on a dry skin, and they help cleanse an oily skin. There is more discussion of oils in Chapter 3, but for regular massage (i.e. without aromatherapy oils), an oil such as sunflower, safflower, almond or even avocado is normally used on its own. You can however mix essential oils with ordinary massage media: once again, the Romans did it all the time. Lavender oil is particularly popular.

Alternative media include talcum powder and cold cream, both of which are recommended for hairy bodies. They make life easier for the masseur, but they do not confer the same benefits as oils, and talcum should never be used on dry skin.

To remove cold cream or talcum (or oils, for that matter, though these are normally left on the skin), you can use eau-de-cologne or skin toner — but be careful, because if these get in the wrong places, the results are hardly sensuous!

Because massage has such a strong instinctive basis, it is (or should be) very safe: you should not be able to harm anyone if you use it with feeling and sensitivity. Awareness is the key: always ask yourself if you would want someone to do to you, what you are doing to them. Ask your partner whether they want you to be firmer or less firm, and make sure they tell you if you do anything that hurts! What you are doing should feel good; if it doesn't, then either you are doing something wrong, or a particular technique is simply not appropriate with that person at that time.

There are also certain conditions where massage is inappropriate; or at least, where certain types of massage are inappropriate. Pregnancy is an obvious area where you need to be very careful indeed: any form of massage is inappropriate in the first three months, and you should avoid massaging the ankles, the lower back and the pelvic area throughout the pregnancy. Abdominal massage should be avoided during menstruation, and if you or you partner has any medical conditions (including diabetes, heart disease, or anything where increased blood flow could create problems), consult your doctor before carrying out any kind of massage. Avoid recent scar tissue (under nine months), recent fractures, varicose veins, inflamed areas, bruises and areas of delicate skin, especially where the skin is close to a bone.

Opposite: Facial massages soothe away stress and headaches, and can also reduce 'worry lines' and keep a youthful complexion for longer — quite apart from being enjoyable in their own right. This is true whether your partner massages your face for you, or whether you do it yourself.

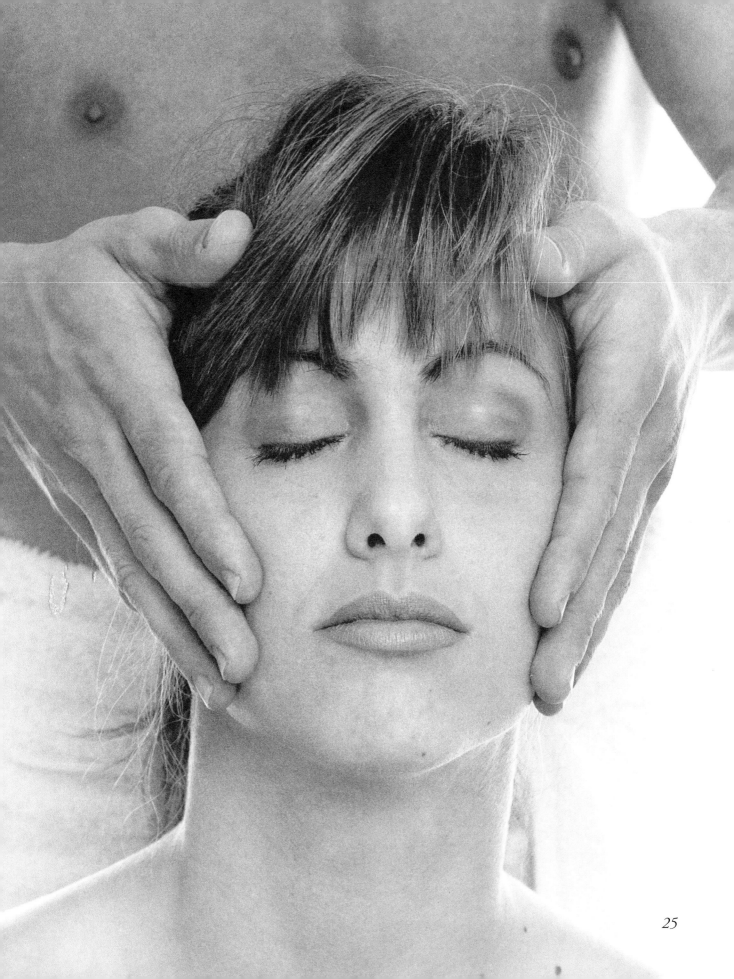

SHIATSU

SHIATSU IS OFTEN regarded as a branch of massage, and indeed it must have the same historical roots, but it has followed a completely different line of development. The word itself derives from the Japanese *shia*, finger, and *tsu*, pressure, and this is an accurate description of what it is: a system of finger pressure on numerous fixed points on the human body. According to classical shiatsu theory, these points are located on 'meridians' through which bodily energy flows, and pressure on the shiatsu points either redirects this energy or releases blockages.

The pressures required are not necessarily very strong, and indeed some are more akin to 'laying on of hands' than anything else. Merely because the theory of meridians in shiatsu is similar to the theory of meridians in acupuncture, some people seem to imagine that you have to use your fingers like acupuncture needles!

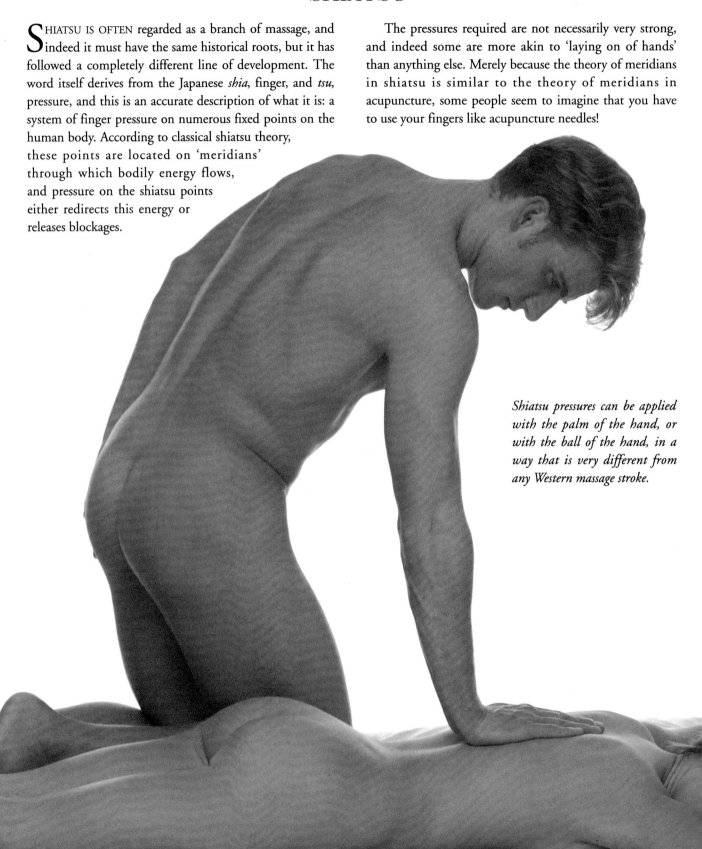

Shiatsu pressures can be applied with the palm of the hand, or with the ball of the hand, in a way that is very different from any Western massage stroke.

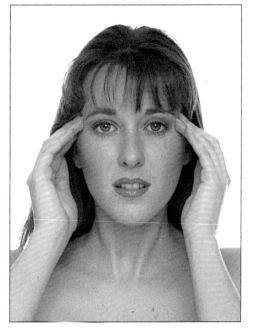

Pressure on shiatsu points is supplemented by manipulation or passive exercise of the joints and muscles, and learning all the shiatsu points and manipulations requires a long course of study, especially if you want to go into the spiritual theory behind the practice. If you do not go into this theory, you are missing much of the point of shiatsu, because it is very much a holistic process grounded in mediaeval Japanese thought. Mind, body and spirit are treated in a holistic manner.

In practice, many shiatsu points may also be used in Western whole-body massage. Some, such as the ones in the neck and shoulders, seem to be located almost instinctively: the kind of massage described on pages 22 and 23 uses several shiatsu points, without formally identifying them. Other shiatsu points are unexpected in both location and function: a point just below the knee, for example, is supposed to help stop travel sickness!

The problem with shiatsu is that if you hit the wrong places, you can actually make things worse instead of better. Although there are many reassuringly clear-looking illustrations of the locations of shiatsu points, if you compare two different charts it soon becomes obvious that the location of the points is by no means as clear-cut as it first seems. This is all the more true when you try to locate them on your partner.

On the other hand, once you have located a shiatsu point correctly, even a very gentle pressure should have some effect; and if it does, then next time you do it you can increase the pressure with a fair degree of confidence, if you think fit. If, on the other hand, you are making the recipient feel worse, you are in the wrong place. With many shiatsu points, quite considerable pressure is applied, usually through the balls of the thumbs, and sometimes even with the heel of the hand. Some shiatsu practitioners will use a considerable proportion of their body weight to exert pressure.

Shiatsu points which are shared with Western massage include the three points on each temple, in line with the corner of the eyes; the six points on the nape of the neck, three on either side; and the numerous points around the lumbar and sacral vertebrae. There are many more, and you do not necessarily need to know their theoretical locations or functions in order to use them.

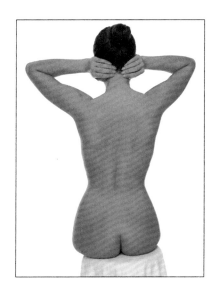

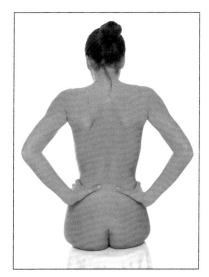

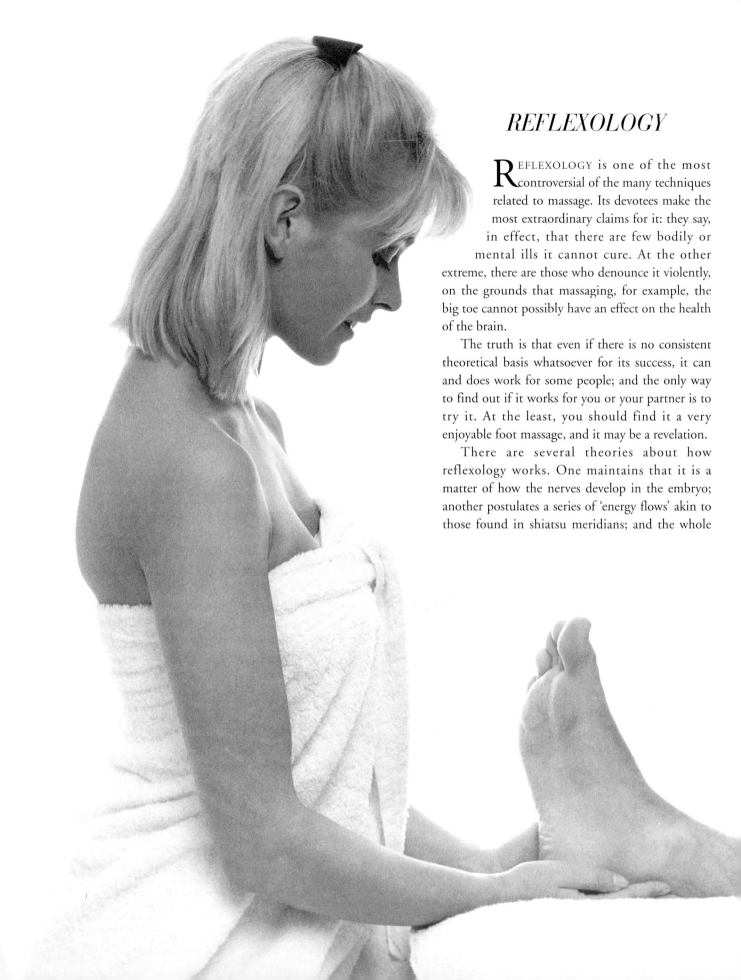

REFLEXOLOGY

REFLEXOLOGY is one of the most controversial of the many techniques related to massage. Its devotees make the most extraordinary claims for it: they say, in effect, that there are few bodily or mental ills it cannot cure. At the other extreme, there are those who denounce it violently, on the grounds that massaging, for example, the big toe cannot possibly have an effect on the health of the brain.

The truth is that even if there is no consistent theoretical basis whatsoever for its success, it can and does work for some people; and the only way to find out if it works for you or your partner is to try it. At the least, you should find it a very enjoyable foot massage, and it may be a revelation.

There are several theories about how reflexology works. One maintains that it is a matter of how the nerves develop in the embryo; another postulates a series of 'energy flows' akin to those found in shiatsu meridians; and the whole term 'reflexology' is based on the assertion that internal organs are 'reflected' on the skin. Strictly speaking, reflexology can be applied to the whole body, though in practice it is normally confined to the hands and feet, and some reflexologists concern themselves only with the feet.

Although many extravagant claims are made for the antiquity of reflexology, in its modern form it is the discovery (or invention) of the American William Fitzgerald, who developed his theories as early as 1915. His ideas were further developed and elaborated by another American, Eunice Ingam, in the 1930s. Outside the United States, it did not make much headway until well after World War Two.

To perform reflexology make sure that both you and your partner are comfortable, with your partner's leg fully supported. Holding their foot on a towel on your lap is ideal. You may use a little talcum if you partner's foot is damp, but oils and creams are never used in reflexology.

Begin by relaxing the foot, holding it between your hands. Move it back and forth and from side to side several times, quite quickly, taking the foot to the limit of its comfortable travel. Supporting the ankle with one hand, pivot the foot on the ankle using a circular motion. Repeat several times. Then try the techniques shown below.

If you find that reflexology works for you, then buy a book on it: this will show specific techniques, how to massage the upper part of the foot, and how to massage the hands. At this level, reflexology is more of a therapeutic technique than a sensual one, and need not be covered in more depth here.

Hold the foot with one hand, and the toes in the other, as shown. Gently flex the toes towards you, exerting a counter-pressure with the thumb. As you flex the toes repeatedly, inch the thumb of your other hand sideways across the instep.

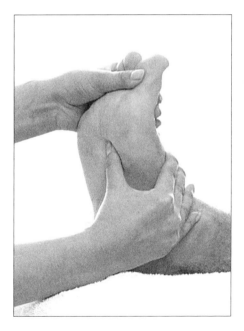

To massage the sole of the foot, hold the toes with the thumb underneath, in the groove between the ball of the foot and the pads of the toes, and 'walk' the front part of ball of the thumb forwards (i.e. towards the toes) over the reflex area chosen.

CHAPTER 3

Aromatherapy

THE SKIN IS the largest organ of the body — and arguably, the most sensuous. After all, what do you think of when you hear the word 'sensuous'? You think of skin… The skin has countless nerve endings which respond to a wide variety of stimuli. These include heat, cold, touch, pain, and even perhaps proximity: we can sense when something is near our skin before it begins to touch, even when there is no temperature differential. Skin is almost magical.

The sense of smell is equally far-reaching, and some would say that it was equally sensuous. The fabled scents of Araby, the biblical frankincense and myrrh; these are synonyms for sensuality and luxury. Again, we have all had the experience of some slight drifting fragrance which brings back a distant memory; we can re-create in our minds some long-gone moment, complete in every detail, from what is, when viewed dispassionately, nothing more than a few complex molecules borne on the breeze. Magic, again.

Some essential oils seem to have more affinity with men, and some with women. This is very much a matter of how they interact with your personal chemistry, however, and it is essential to experiment with a range of oils to see which ones suit you best. An oil often recommended for men is sandalwood; for women, jasmine is popular.

phenomena, and more. The skin can absorb oils and volatile chemicals astonishingly quickly, in minutes or even seconds, and things which are absorbed through the skin can have profound physiological effects. The development of nicotine patches for giving up smoking is a modern example; aromatherapy, by contrast, has been around for centuries.

Aromatherapy is, therefore, a great deal more than just a matter of finding things which smell nice, and then rubbing

them on your body. The essential oils which are used in aromatherapy should of course please the sense of smell; but they do a lot of other things as well.

Beginning with the sense of smell, it is no news that some odours are pleasant, relaxing, or even medicinal; eucalyptus oil is famous for clearing a stuffy nose. Nor is it news that different oils react differently with different people. This is, after all, why there are so many different varieties of perfume. What smells wonderful on one person can smell downright unpleasant on another; and, almost equally important, what smells wonderful to one person can smell awful to another.

Essential oils must therefore be used with care and discretion. But there is more reason to be careful than just personal preference — though this should not be underrated. Essential oils, which are distilled from a wide variety of plant sources, have definite physiological effects. Undiluted, they are often powerful antiseptics, and are occasionally used a drop at a time for this purpose. However, this is likely to be a risky and extravagant way of using them: some undiluted oils can provoke severe skin reactions, and there can be all sorts of other effects, from headaches to nausea.

If they are to be rubbed on the skin they are therefore used diluted, typically in concentrations of a couple of drops of essential oil to a teaspoon (5 ml) of carrier oil such as almond oil or grapeseed oil — though dilutions for massaging small children, or for adults with sensitive skins, might be as little as one fifth of this strength. Essential oils are definitely not a case of 'more is better'.

What, though, are 'essential oils', and how do they work? The first of these two questions is much easier to answer than the second one.

As already mentioned, they are distilled or otherwise concentrated from plants. Although there are several thousand plants which can be distilled to

yield essential oils, modern aromatherapy is built around less than fifty of these.

They are distilled in a number of ways, and in many countries. In India, where essential oils have been distilled for centuries and form a part of ancient ayurvedic therapies, the smell of a country eucalyptus oil distillery is unforgettable. The plants are usually very carefully selected: even lavender oil, one of the most familiar oils in the West, can only be distilled for aromatherapy purposes from a very limited number of species of lavender plant. Other techniques of extracting essential oils are also used: some are effective but slow, expensive and time consuming, while others are efficient but use harsh solvents which can result in inferior oils.

Because they are distilled, essential oils are very highly concentrated — though some are more concentrated than others. The best qualities can be very expensive indeed, but they will be extremely pure because they are distilled from the finest original materials without any adulteration, and because distillation is carried out at carefully controlled temperatures to ensure that only the required oils are extracted.

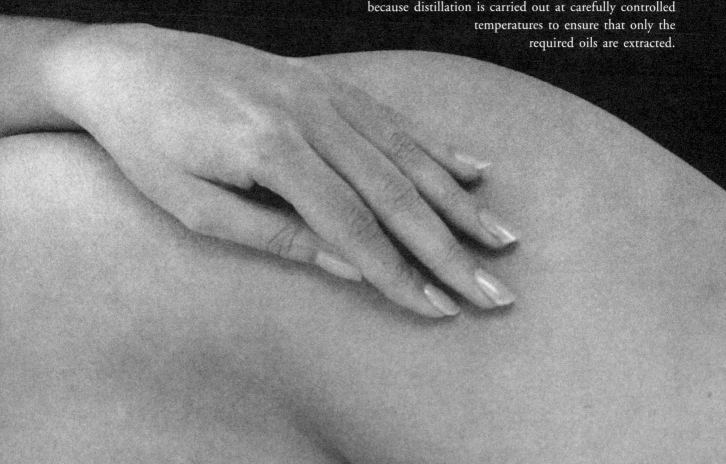

The amount of raw material required to produce high quality oils can be quite extraordinary: an armful of plant material may distill down to a tiny bottle of essential oil.

Although the best oils are very expensive, they are generally worth the money. Adulterated or synthetic oils may have no effect at all, or worse still, they may have adverse effects. The best oils are sold in small dark glass bottles, typically 10 ml: rather under half a fluid ounce, or a couple of teaspoonsful. There is no sense in buying larger quantities, as the life of essential oils is finite: depending on how they are stored, it is usually only a few months. Oils which are stored in a cool, dark place will last longer than those which are stored somewhere warm and bright, which is why brown glass bottles are normally used. Also, they soon oxidize, so the bottles should always be stoppered tightly. An essential oil in a clear glass bottle on a sunny window-sill might be useless after a few days; in an open bottle in the same position, it could well be useless in a few hours. Also, although there may be a few highly specialized plastics which would be suitable, most pure oils will react quickly and unfavourably with most plastics. If you buy the ready-diluted oils which are available from some cosmetics suppliers, you can save a fair amount of money, and there is no problem with the plastic bottles that they are supplied in; but you are not buying very much essential oil at a time, because most of it is carrier oil.

As for how they work, you can take either a mystical or a scientific approach. Scientifically, there is no doubt that all kinds of interesting stereochemistries are involved, with receptor sites in the brain and elsewhere; but this is the sort of subject you could study for a lifetime. Mystically, all you can say is that they do work — or to be more accurate, they can work; which is what matters for a sensual massage.

Self-massage with essential oils can be done in many ways, but a useful technique is to put a single drop of your favourite essential oil on a moistened loofah bath mitt or a soft, natural bristle body brush, before you take your bath or shower. Brush yourself all over, with long, sweeping strokes. Be gentle, especially in winter or if your skin is dry or sensitive, and discontinue IMMEDIATELY if you have any skin reaction.

CHOOSING ESSENTIAL OILS

You do not need to buy all of the essential oils in the modern aromatherapy canon. Few people, for example, would want to use garlic oil, or even eucalyptus oil, which is one of the oils which gives traditional liniments their strong smell. Having said that, personal taste is enormously important, and if you like eucalyptus oil, then use it!

For a sensual massage, you may want to try some or all of the oils listed below, either singly or in combination. It is worth pointing out, however, that the smell of an oil diluted for massage can be very different from the smell of that same oil in concentrated form. Quite often, concentrated oils are overwhelming and indeed almost repellent; but those same oils, mixed with an appropriate carrier, can be extremely sensuous.

It is also worth pointing out that while you may wish to try all sorts of combinations of oils, you cannot adopt a 'cook-book' approach. If, for example, you mixed together all the alleged aphrodisiacs, you might end up with something which smelled, and felt, far from sensuous.

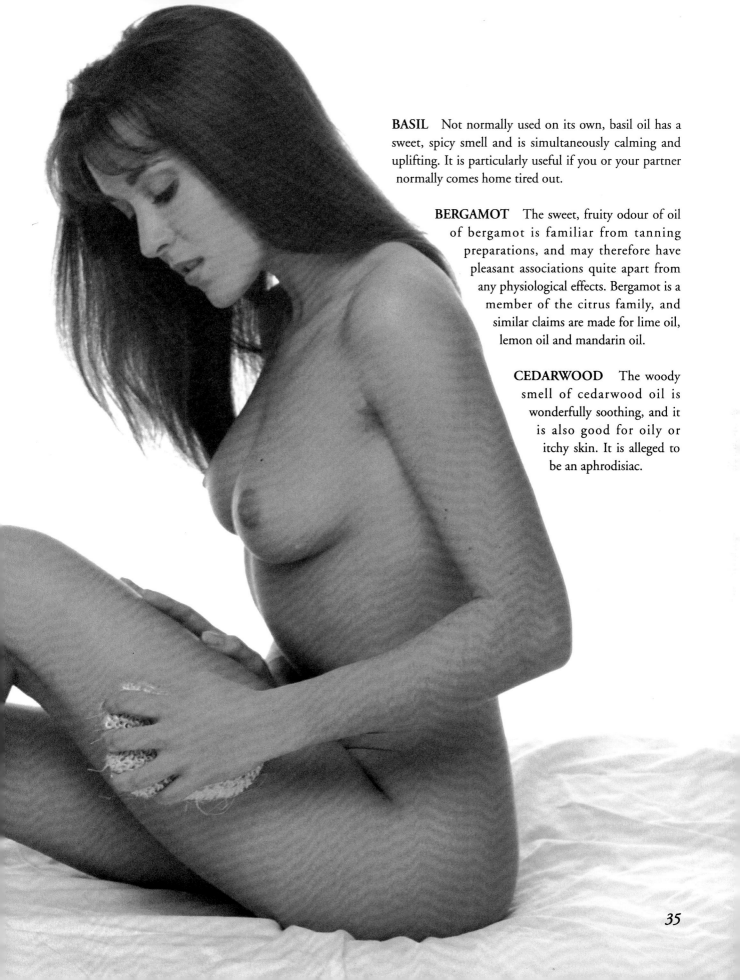

BASIL   Not normally used on its own, basil oil has a sweet, spicy smell and is simultaneously calming and uplifting. It is particularly useful if you or your partner normally comes home tired out.

BERGAMOT   The sweet, fruity odour of oil of bergamot is familiar from tanning preparations, and may therefore have pleasant associations quite apart from any physiological effects. Bergamot is a member of the citrus family, and similar claims are made for lime oil, lemon oil and mandarin oil.

CEDARWOOD   The woody smell of cedarwood oil is wonderfully soothing, and it is also good for oily or itchy skin. It is alleged to be an aphrodisiac.

Massage and aromatherapy are, to some extent, 'separate but equal'. A neck and shoulders massage will relieve tension; but combine it with, say, a lavender and neroli bath, and the effect will be very much greater.

CINNAMON Another alleged aphrodisiac, cinnamon oil has a warm, spicy smell but must be diluted considerably to avoid skin reactions.

CLARY SAGE Neither of the authors actually likes this, but we both know other people who swear by it. It is very relaxing and indeed sedative; some people even avoid driving after using it.

CLOVE Most people know this as a specific for toothache, but in combination with other oils it can be very heady; it is a stimulant and, once again, is sometimes touted as an aphrodisiac.

FRANKINCENSE Prized since biblical times, frankincense can be distilled to give 'olibanum'. It is normally heated over a small burner rather than used as a massage oil, but as a massage oil it can promote an extraordinary feeling of luxury and well-being which is only partially due to knowing what it costs. If any essential oil is an elixir of youth, this is it.

GERANIUM Calming and cooling, it reduces anxiety and tension and is good for dry skin.

GINGER Ginger oil must be well diluted, and even then, it is a warming and stimulating oil. It goes surprisingly well with lemon balm oil (see opposite).

JASMINE Those who like jasmine oil, love it. Others (a minority) find it sickly. If you like it, you can expect relaxation and a general sense of well-being. It is also good for dry skin.

JUNIPER Good for oily skin, and for the circulation. If the smell seems familiar, it may be because juniper berries are the chief flavouring agent in gin.

LAVENDER If this were not an alphabetical list, lavender would come at the very top. The most widely used and widely liked of all essential oils, it is good for the nervous system and restores energy, as well as speeding healing. It is often combined with other oils, and mixes well with almost all of them. Avoid temptations to over use, which can result in bad dreams and poor sleep.

LEMON BALM (MELISSA)   This uplifting, calming oil is distilled from a plant known in many countries as 'Heart's Delight'.

MYRRH   Strictly for traditionalists, this one; a resinous and memorable oil, but not one that many people enjoy.

NEROLI   Also known as orange flower oil, this is distilled from the blossoms of bitter oranges; it is something of a panacea in many Near Eastern countries. It is good for dry skin and has a calming, tranquillizing effect.

PATCHOULI   Beloved of hippies, patchouli is good for the skin and is reputed to be an aphrodisiac.

PEPPERMINT   Noted principally for its cooling and refreshing properties, this is an oil which some people find very stimulating and others find altogether too hearty in the context of a sensual massage.

ROSE   Like jasmine, this powerfully floral oil is very good for those who like it; but not everyone does, and it is extremely expensive. It is said to be cooling, soothing, toning, and good for the sex drive.

SAGE   Stimulating and restorative, sage is very good for muscular aches and pains. The smell is not to everyone's taste and it should be masked with something else.

A long, sensuous leg and foot massage is extremely relaxing, and can be erotic; but combine it with, say, a ylang-ylang aromatherapy massage and the senses will be heightened; ylang-ylang is said to be an aphrodisiac.

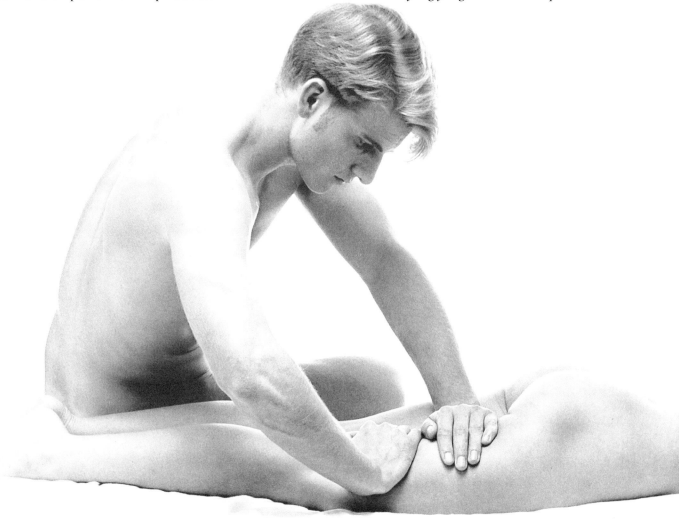

SANDALWOOD   Yet another oil claimed as an aphrodisiac, sandalwood is also good for dry skin and for rejuvenating aging skin.

VETIVER   Rarely encountered on its own, vetiver is responsible for what perfumers call 'grassy notes', but it is also a calming agent which is excellent when used with chamomile.

YLANG-YLANG   Somewhat improbably claimed as both a sedative to the nervous system and an aphrodisiac, ylang-ylang is almost unbearably musky at full strength, but can be very relaxing when diluted for use. It is made from individual flowers, hand-picked at dawn in Indonesia — a truly exotic essential oil.

Massage strokes for aromatherapy are often gentler than those used in conventional massage, and it is even more important to keep the hands conforming to the body's contours as you spread the oil over your partner's body. A technique that is often used, for example, in a

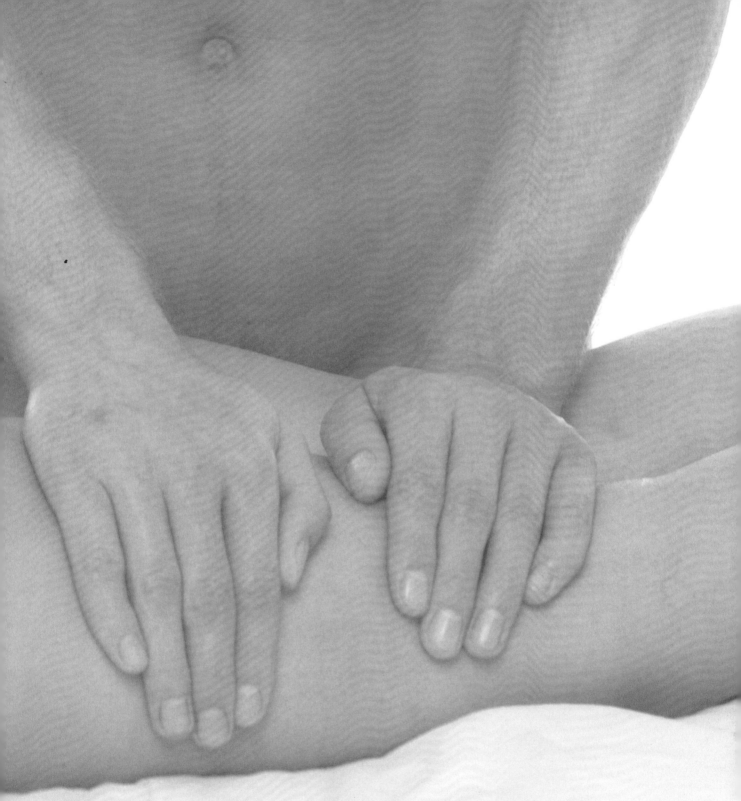

massage which begins at the neck and passes from there to the shoulder to the arm, is a continuous alternate stroking movement, following the circumference of the curve for a few inches. This is then repeated with a fractional move to the side.

It is a mistake to imagine that there is no place for firmness in aromatherapy massage. The real difference between aromatherapy massage and conventional massage is that there is much more emphasis on constant hand contact, with little or no percussive movement.

CARRIER OILS

You can use almost any vegetable oil as a carrier for essential oils, but some smell (and feel) very much more agreeable than others. Cold-pressed oils are best; you should avoid hot-pressed or processed oils if at all possible. Sunflower, safflower and even soy oils are quite adequate, and readily available. Grapeseed oil is only a little harder to find, and is also suitable, though more exotic oils add a touch of luxury and have pleasant aromas in their own right. Almond oil is traditional; avocado oil is excellent; and some people like to add wheat germ oil to anything used on the face, because of its high vitamin content. After this, you are into the realms of the exotic, the personal, and the historical. Olive oil is what the Greeks and Romans would have used. Sesame oil is favoured by some, though good sesame oil is strong-smelling. Mustard oil is widely used in India, but the smell is a little too much for most people outside the Sub-Continent.

USING OILS IN AROMATHERAPY

From a sensuous point of view, the three main ways to use essential oils are in a heater, to aromatize a room; in a bath, as a bath oil; and in massage.

Heaters or 'burners' should not burn the oil, but should heat a few drops gently, often in warm water; in fact, a warm radiator can supply all the heat you need to vaporize an essential oil. In a bath, you should use only a few drops: three to five drops is a good starting point, though you may need more or less depending on the size of your bath and on the oil you use. Add the oil drop by drop when you are in the bath — but mix it well and do not get neat oil on your skin, especially on sensitive areas. Once again, avoid the 'more is better' approach: remember, you are absorbing the oil through the pores of your skin (which are opened by the heat), and you are breathing the vapour.

As for massage, aromatherapy massage differs from other types of massage in that it is a combination of traditional Swedish-inspired massage with a more intuitive approach. The principal concern is to apply the oil to the skin in such a way that the essential oils will be absorbed.

An aromatherapy massage, because it is so intuitive, can be almost like dancing with your hands on your partner's body. Some aromatherapy strokes break the rules of conventional massage completely, by carrying out such movements as up the back ... along the arms ... and then across the hands, finally leaving the fingertips behind as the masseur's (or masseuse's) hands move outwards. The broad, smooth area of the back is very receptive to the absorption of essential oils, as well as being an area where a lot of tension builds up. It is, therefore, an ideal place to massage aromatherapy oils into the skin. The most useful movement is to start just above the buttocks, with one hand on either side of the spine. Move the hands upwards to the shoulder-blades, then outwards so that your hands are now on either side of the torso. With a gentle, conforming stroke, move your hands down the body until they are level with the top of the buttocks, then without lifting your hands from your partner's skin return to the starting position.

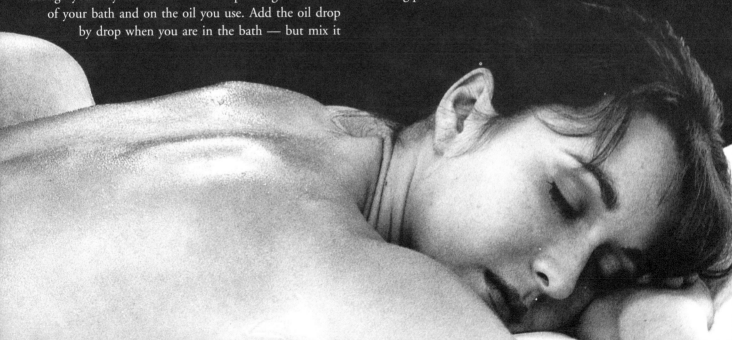

CHAPTER 4

Where and
WHEN

BEFORE YOU START to practise your massage skills, you need somewhere comfortable to do so. The bedroom is an obvious choice, but it is not always the best. In particular, if you have a soft bed, it is suitable only for a relatively limited range of massage techniques. This is not so much for the comfort of the person receiving the massage, as for the comfort of the person giving it. A bed is just the wrong height for standing up to give a massage, and if you try kneeling on the bed to give the massage, you may find that you fall over a lot. This can be fun, but does not help much with the massage. Even if you don't fall over, you may end up with an aching back.

A firm bed, or better still a futon, is much more satisfactory. Alternatively, the floor is fine, but spread something that is soft and comfortable to lie on — not a woollen carpet, for example. Use something which you do not mind getting massage oil on: a big bath towel, which is easily washed and which will not take an oil stain, is ideal. Satin sheets are not!

It is a good idea, in fact, to buy a towel set, or even two or three sets specifically for this purpose. You want an extra large bath towel to lie on; two or three smaller towels to fold into pads, to support the body of the person receiving the massage; and ideally another large towel or two to keep your partner warm. The person giving the massage will be less inclined to get cold, because he or she will be moving around.

If you get really serious about massage — even sensual massage — you may want to consider a massage table, which is easily the most convenient and relaxing surface for both the giver of the massage and the receiver; but it is not something you will need (or even want) to buy at first.

As for the ideal room in which to give or receive a massage, the bedroom is once again the most obvious choice but not necessarily the best.

What you want is comfort; privacy; an agreeable ambience; and freedom from distraction. The main criterion for comfort is a reasonable and uniform temperature. In a cold climate, an open fire can be very welcome, while in a hot climate, you may bless an air conditioner; but the fire is not much fun if it is the only source of heat in a chilly room, and the air conditioner is generally more agreeable if you do not need to stand in its icy blast in order to be comfortable. Apart from keeping the room at the right temperature, you also need the right

light level: neither uncomfortably bright, nor so dark that you keep falling over things. As with the temperature, the lighting should be evenly distributed: the last thing you need is a bright light glaring in the eyes of either person. Candlelight can be good.

Privacy is self-explanatory, though there may be more to it than is immediately obvious. A locked door will keep people out, and curtains will stop them staring through the windows; but this is not necessarily much use if the doorbell keeps ringing, or if you can hear people's conversations immediately outside your window. Try to choose a time which will be reasonably free from interruption, and unless you are worried about missing phone calls, either disconnect the phone (or turn off the ringer), or put a cushion over the answering machine.

Ambience is a much more personal matter. For example, some people can imagine few things more relaxing than soft music. Others find few things more irritating. By all means play whatever you like, but make sure that your partner agrees with your selection; listening to music you don't like, just to please someone else, is a major turn-off. Likewise, you may want to burn some incense or to vaporize some essential aromatherapy oil. Again, make sure that you both agree.

Finally, we have already mentioned distractions such as the telephone and the doorbell, but there are plenty of others, many of which can be self-inflicted. For example, don't set your self-timing oven, or your radio alarm. Both can place such constraints on your time that you never relax fully. Even if you allow, say, two hours, when you only expect to spend one hour on the massage, there is always the sense of the taxi-meter running; and this can be deeply off-putting.

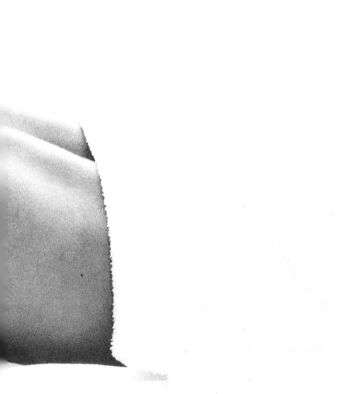

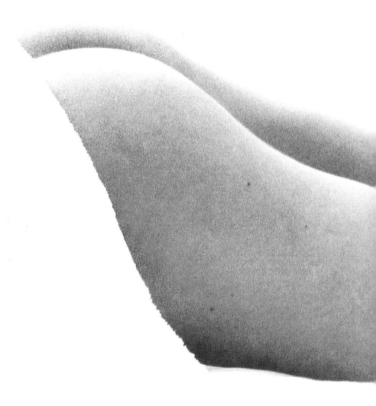

GETTING YOURSELF READY

How you prepare yourself for a sensuous massage session will depend on you, your partner, and your life-style. If one of you gets home before the other, take the trouble to make a small romantic gesture: a single long-stemmed rose with the kiss at the door, or a favourite drink ready-mixed. By all means plan a romantic meal, either at home or in a restaurant. Eat food that you like, but do not eat very much of it; you are eating for pleasure, not satiety. By the same token, by all means drink a little champagne or whatever else you like and can afford; but stay reasonably sober!

A bath or a shower before the massage is a virtual necessity, especially if you have been out working all day. Being fresh and clean makes the massage much more sensual and uninhibited, and the bath or shower can be fun in its own right; sharing a bath is an ancient intimacy, and what a shower lacks in relaxation it can make up in entertainment value. Do not forget the possibility of adding essential oils to the bath water, as described on page 41, or of dry-brushing, as described on page 34. On the other hand, do not overdo the essential oils: if you try one in the bath, another in an oil heater, and yet another in the massage oil, you can find that they clash and create a mood which is far from sensuous. You can even overdose, literally: too many essential oils, mixed indiscriminately or used to excess, can give you headaches and make you feel unwell.

Trim your fingernails and keep them clean. If you use nail varnish, make sure that it is clean and fresh. The skin of your hands should be soft, not chapped and rough; use hand creams if you have to. If you have any cuts or scratches on your hands, look carefully at where they are and ask yourself if they will interfere with the pleasure of either giving or receiving a massage.

Remove all jewellery, except (if you insist) your wedding ring. The dangers of loose, dangling bracelets and necklaces are obvious, both for the giver of the massage and the receiver; but even tight bracelets and necklaces can give rise to unexpected discomforts and pinches when they are worn by the giver, quite apart from the problems they can create by getting in the way when someone is receiving a massage. The same is true of ear-rings; small studs are a much better idea than big, dangling ear-rings, but even then, the back of the ear-ring can scratch the neck of the person receiving the massage, or the hands of the person giving it.

How much (or how little) clothing you wear is very much a matter of personal choice. The person receiving the massage should preferably be nude, though large towels are useful for keeping warm: if you are lying still and receiving a massage, the areas which are not being massaged can get surprisingly cold, surprisingly quickly. One thing you do not want to have to do is keep interrupting the massage to remove (or replace) clothes. The person giving the massage can wear loose, non-constricting clothes, which should not have flowing sleeves or other draperies — or, of course, he or she can wear nothing at all.

CHAPTER 5

How To Use Your Hands In
MASSAGE

ALMOST ANY FORM OF TOUCH — even a hand laid upon another's, without movement — is to some extent a form of massage. Massage is, after all, touch. Gentleness, communication, healing; all these qualities are, or can be, expressed in touch. Although the hands are the point of contact, they are an expression of your whole personality and intention; they must be gentle, yet strong, and they should not make sudden, unexpected movements. The movements of your hands should flow in a continuous, loving manner.

In massage, there are three main groups or kinds of touching. The first is stroking, or effleurage. The second is kneading, or petrissage. And the third is percussion, or tapotement.

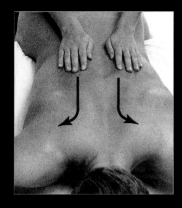 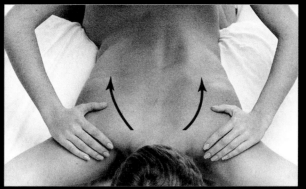 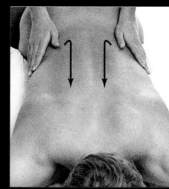

A back massage illustrates well the effleurage technique. Place your hands on either side of the spine just below the waist and push your hands away from you with firm pressure; lean forward to allow your body weight to follow the stroke. Make sure that your palms and fingers conform to your partner's body contours at all times.

At the top of the stroke, move your hands outwards to follow the shape of the shoulders, almost in a heart shape, with your palms leading the movement towards the sides and your fingers following.

Finally, make the link movement to return to the starting position, keeping your whole hand in contact with your partner's skin, using a very light stroke and keeping your hands parallel with your partner's spine. You can repeat this stroke several times, gradually moving your hands further and further out to the side of your partner's trunk.

EFFLEURAGE

EFFLEURAGE can be light ('superficial') or firm ('deep'). Either way, it should be gentle; massage should never be crudely forceful. The gentle strokes are used for applying the massage oil, and to set the tone for the massage; to establish that it is a means of communication, of being in contact with one another. They are also used as linking or return strokes, in conjunction with the firmer or deeper strokes which relax the muscles, stimulate the circulation, improve the skin, and generally do the things that a massage is supposed to do. Linking strokes are important because they maintain the contact and communication: suddenly breaking contact by lifting your hand can be surprisingly distressing for the person on the receiving end of a massage.

In effleurage, you generally use the

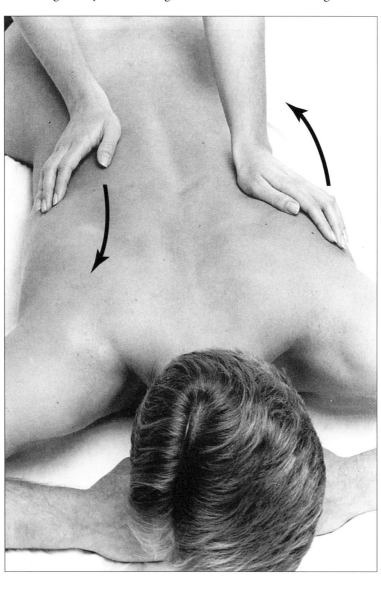

whole of the palm of the hand, together with the fingers, though in some of the lighter strokes such as 'cat strokes' (using each hand in turn, rather in the way that a cat sharpens its claws), you may just trail your fingertips along your partner's body.

Because effleurage is the most basic and indeed instinctive form of massage, it is the easiest to learn; and it would be possible, for instance, to give a pleasurable and sensual aromatherapy massage without using any other strokes.

Instead of using both hands simultaneously, as described in the previous three pictures, you can stroke with each hand alternately. The upward stroke, towards your partner's neck, is firm, and as one hand is doing this, the other is returning with a light gliding motion. You repeat these strokes several times, to get a good flowing rhythm.

Another variation on the basic stroke is the fan stroke. As you move your hands up the muscles of the back, you move them outwards in a fan shape, like a very abbreviated version of the basic stroke. Mould your hands to conform to the contours of the body, following them around to the sides. Glide them down the sides, and without breaking contact, return to a position slightly above your original starting point, repeating the stroke until you have covered the whole back.

The side stroke is a rather different stroke. With your hands loose and relaxed, stroke upwards from the lower part of the side to the upper, towards the spine, using your hands alternately in a slow, rhythmic movement. This movement can also be used on the shoulders and arms, working slowly downwards towards the hand, where you can finish with a gentle release. Side strokes and fan strokes are often used for applying essential oils in aromatherapy.

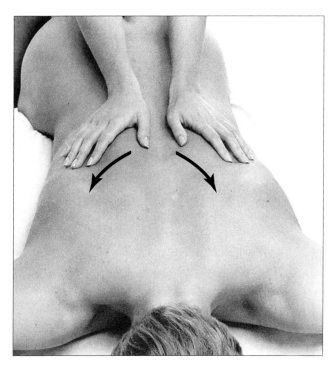

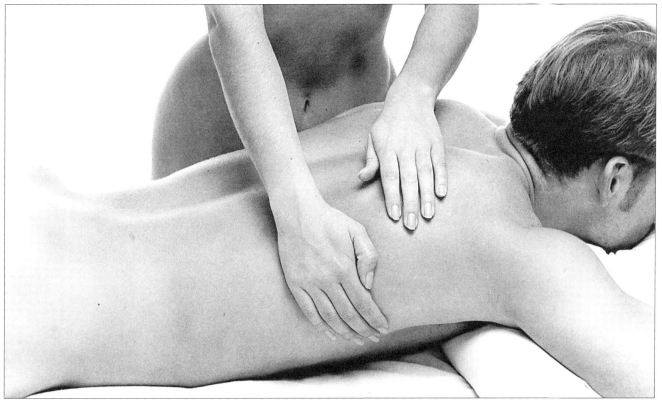

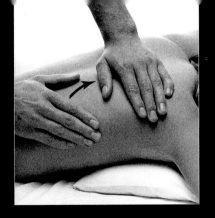 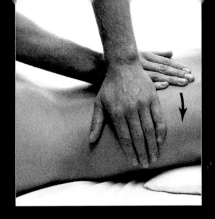 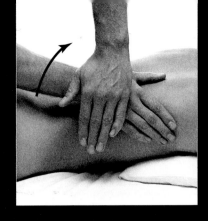

To begin a circle stroke, place both your hands on one side of the back, with one a little higher than the other. Slide the upper hand down with a circular movement, and the lower one upwards; the centre of the circle is between your two hands. Continue in the same clockwise movement, with one hand following the other. When your hands cross, lift one hand over the other, which continues in a circle and remains in contact with the skin. On the right side, lift your left hand over the right and replace it on the skin. Repeat the movement in a series of interlinked circles, moving up the back. When you reach the shoulder-blade, slide both hands down in the same linking stroke as described for basic effleurage; move your hands to the other side; and repeat the same strokes in mirror image, moving in anticlockwise circles. Like so many massage strokes, this is harder to describe than to do!

Circle thumb stroking is similar to making circular strokes with the whole hand, but on a very much smaller scale. Working about an inch (25mm) from the spine, and beginning in the small of the back, make small, circular movements with your thumbs, pushing the muscles away from the spine. Slowly work up first one side of the spine, and then the other.

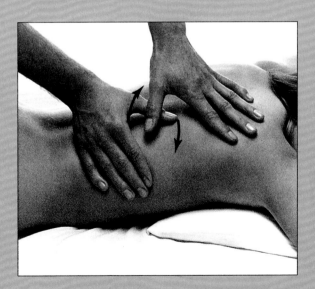

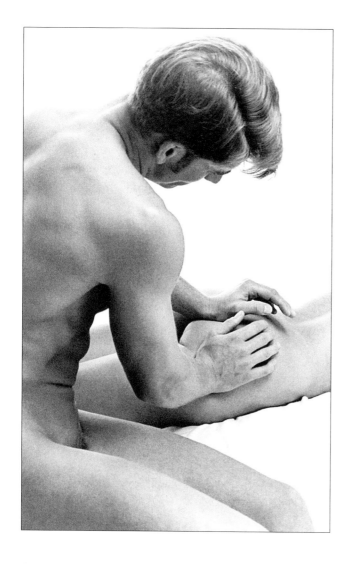

PETRISSAGE

PETRISSAGE covers a multitude of movements, but they are all forms of pressure or plucking: muscles and other soft tissues are either compressed towards a bone, or are lifted from a bone.

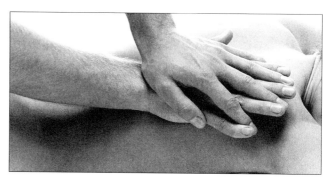

Kneading is pushing inwards and upwards against the resistance of a bone, using the palm of the hand in a circular movement. The main pressure occurs as you move your hand upwards; on the downward movement, you relax the pressure and move the hand slightly sideways to continue the massage. You can use one hand, or both hands alternately. If you want to exert extra pressure, you can use both hands, one on top of the other. You can also use your fingers or thumbs to apply localized kneading movements, especially around joints, to loosen muscle knots and even adhesions.

Wringing is much the same as kneading, with an added twist; as the name suggests, you 'wring' your partner's flesh between your fingers Move your hands alternately, so that the fingers of one hand move towards the thumb of the other, pressing into the flesh as you do so. Move along the area to be massaged, and back again. This is a deep, stimulating stroke which can be used on the side of the body, the arms — anywhere there is enough flesh to get a grip.

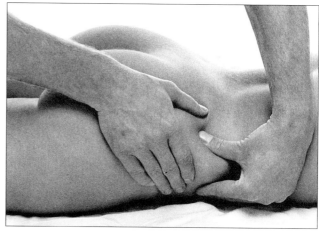

Skin rolling is very relaxing, and much more sensuous than it sounds. It is a movement for the larger areas of the torso. Put simply, you reach across the spine; lay your hands flat; take a double handful of flesh from the side of the body, as gently as you can; then 'walk' your fingers backwards towards your thumbs, gradually releasing the roll that you are holding. Repeat, with your hands moved slightly closer or further away from you, until you have worked over the entire area to be covered.

Picking up is exactly what its name suggests: a roll of flesh is picked up between the thumb and and all the fingers, with the wrist turned so that the fingers are parallel with the surface being picked up. You use a rolling movement, rotating your wrist away from the bone while picking up the flesh with a gentle squeezing action. Then you relax the grip, move the hand along slightly, and repeat the movement. Picking up is not the same as pinching, which is something you should never do in massage. You can also use both hands together for this movement: instead of using your thumb and finger, you use the fingers of your left hand and the fingers of your right hand, picking up the flesh between them. This is typically used for larger areas, like the thigh.

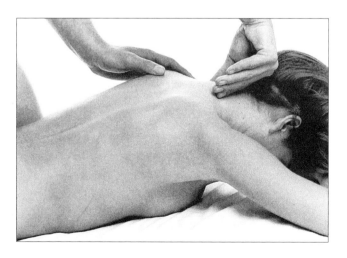

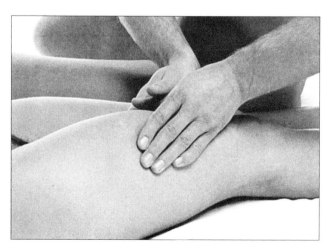

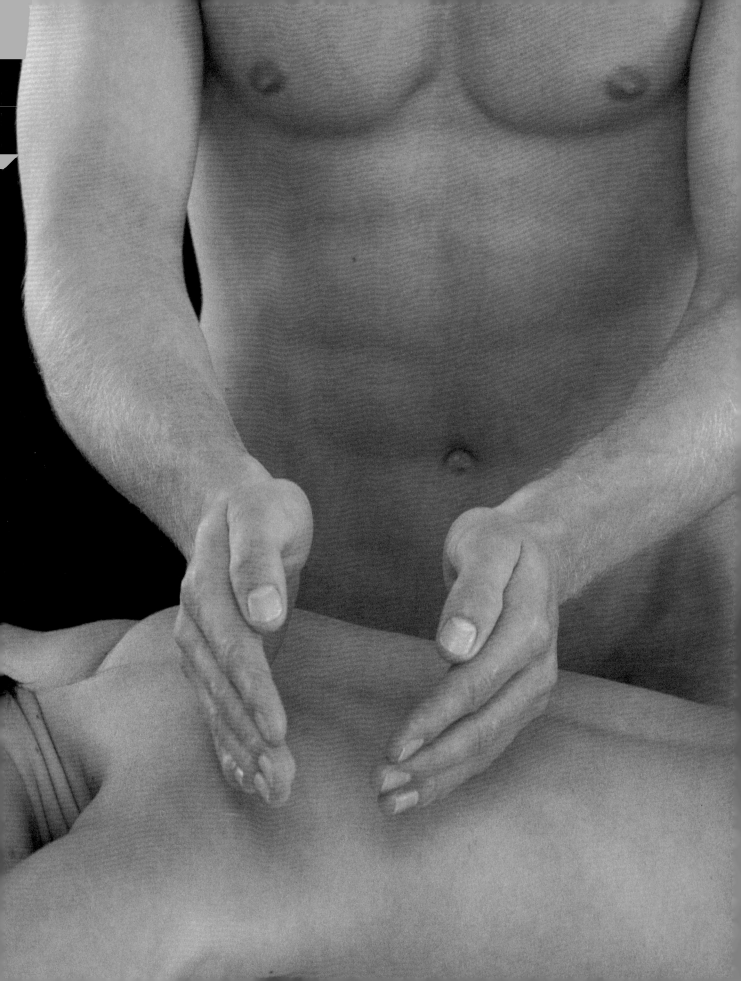

KNEADING AND TAPOTEMENT

KNEADING

Kneading may not seem very sensual when you hear it described, but if it is done properly, it can feel really good. The important thing is to avoid pinching or painful squeezing: you should be very gentle at first, until you gain in confidence and your partner gains in trust. Then, you can exert more pressure without any adverse effects; in fact, exactly the opposite.

The more practised you become at kneading, the better you will become at establishing a smooth, comfortable rhythm; not just the rhythm of your hands, but also that of your whole body. It can become almost like a dance — which is one argument for being highly selective in your choice of music to be played during a massage, in case the rhythm of the music you have chosen does not match the natural rhythm of the massage.

TAPOTEMENT

Just as kneading should be rhythmic, with carefully judged pressure, percussion or 'tapotement' should be light and springy, and not too hard. The secret lies in keeping your movements loose, fluid and mobile. The individual movements, and the way you hold your hands for them, vary widely, so you cannot make too many generalizations: each technique has to be considered separately.

One generalization which can however be made is that you should never do tapotement over bony areas, the abdomen, or the kidneys. Opinions are divided about some other areas: in particular, some professionals are distinctly unhappy about the idea of 'hacking' on the feet. 'Hacking' is the classic massage percussion stroke, which everyone thinks they know about, and which is illustrated opposite; but it is also the hardest to learn to do properly. It is done with the sides of the little fingers and not, as generations of schoolboys have fondly imagined, as a series of karate chops!

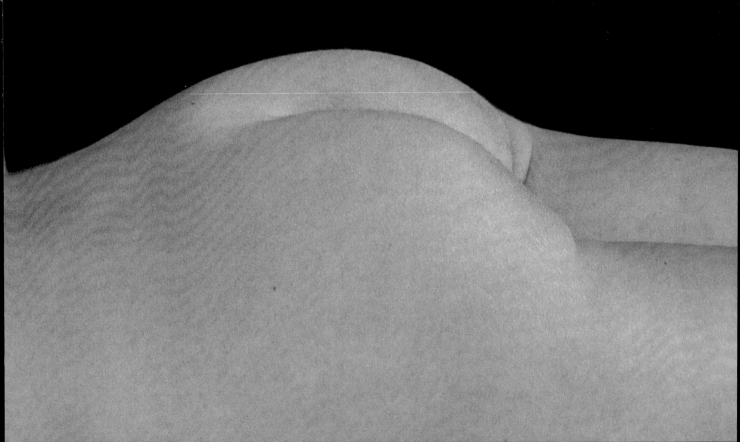

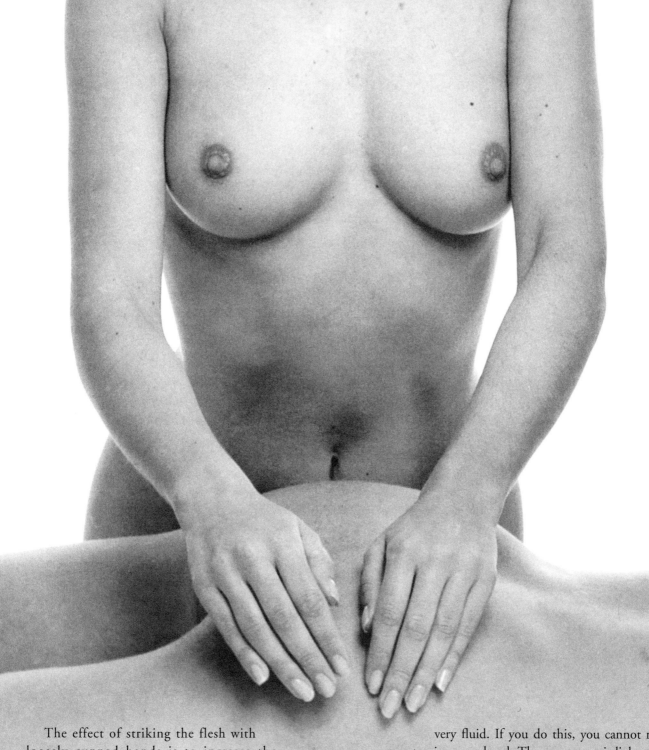

The effect of striking the flesh with loosely cupped hands is to increase the circulation in that part of the body.

Cup your hands with your fingers close together; they must form a cup, and not be too loose, but they must not be rigid either. The important thing is to keep your wrist as free as possible, so that the up-and-down movement is

very fluid. If you do this, you cannot really over-tension your hand. The movement is light, rapid and alternate, with one hand rising as the other descends; the cupped hand must leave the skin quickly and springily. It is easy to tell if you are doing this right, as your hands will make a hollow cupping sound, instead of the slapping sound that you get if you are doing it wrong.

Hacking, pounding and beating all sound alarming, but they are not really. Hacking is done with the sides of the little fingers, and possibly with the tips and sides of the upper part of the ring and middle fingers: the hand is held very loose, and the essential movement is a flicking motion at the wrist, in the plane of the blade of the hand. It is done quickly and

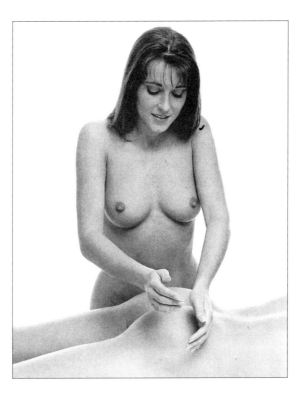

lightly, using the hands alternately. A good way to practise the kind of loose wrist movement that is needed, and to build up a good rhythm from one hand to the other, is to practise on the air: shadow massage, like shadow boxing. Again, you can tell from the sound when you are doing it properly: it should sound like big, heavy raindrops falling fast.

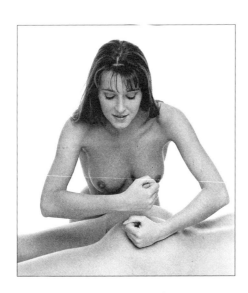

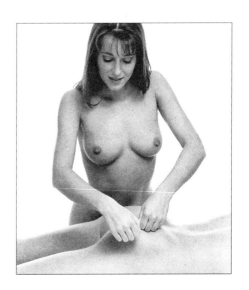

Pounding is a heavier movement, using a loosely clenched fist. The striking part is the side of the fist. The movement is rather different, too. Your fists rotate around one another, in the same sort of movement as when you twiddle your thumbs, and they strike alternately like the blades of a (very blunt!) old-fashioned lawnmower. You advance across the area to be massaged, again rather like pushing the old lawnmower forwards.

Beating is also done with a loosely clenched fist, except that the part that now strikes your partner is the second and third knuckles of the fingers. The movement is from the elbow and wrist, and it is somewhat reminiscent of a faster, percussive version of the cat stroke described on page 52.

Beating should not be done too rapidly — the movement should be at the speed of a steady 'plod'.

CHAPTER 6

Massaging
THE BODY
NECK AND SHOULDERS

A NUMBER OF COMPANIES recognize the value of neck and shoulders massages for stressed executives, and actually hire masseurs to come to the office and massage their senior personnel on a weekly or even daily basis. If you are not far enough up the corporate tree for such luxuries, don't worry: a neck and shoulders massage from your partner will be just as good, and probably a lot more enjoyable.

The simplest form of neck and shoulders massage, with the person receiving the massage sitting in a chair, has already been covered on page 23. A much more effective form of neck and shoulders massage can however be given with the person receiving it lying down, either face down or on their back. All of the techniques of massage are used, with particular emphasis on deep effleurage and thumb pressure. A great deal depends on your ability to feel stiffness and knots in your partner's muscles, and to work on them gently but firmly.

For the massage with your partner lying face down, begin by using the pads of your thumbs to relax the muscles on either side of the spine. With your hands placed naturally on your partner's shoulders, your thumbs will automatically fall in the best place to begin the massage, and your partner will be able to tell you exactly where feels best.

Using firm but gentle upward pressures of your thumbs, move your hands around the area on either side of your partner's spine.

Next, using small rotational movements of the balls of the thumbs, increase the area of the massage, working across the upper part of the shoulders in response to your partner's instructions, feeling for stiff muscles and knots.

When you have finished this, place your hands on either side of your partner's neck, at the top, and stroke down and outwards across the shoulders, using effleurage strokes and keeping your hands in contact with the skin at all times. Apply a firm pressure on the outward stroke; use a lighter pressure as you return. You can also use side strokes (page 53) from the neck to the shoulders.

almost parallel with the skin: merely grabbing a handful and pulling is not what you want, and certainly not what your partner wants.

When you move on to wringing, which requires the use of both hands, you cannot work on both sides at once. Begin on one side of the neck and, move out towards the shoulder and back again; then repeat for the other side.

Finally, put your hands on either side of the nape of the neck and, conforming them closely to the shape of the neck and shoulder, stroke gently outwards towards the shoulders. After the first few strokes, return with the

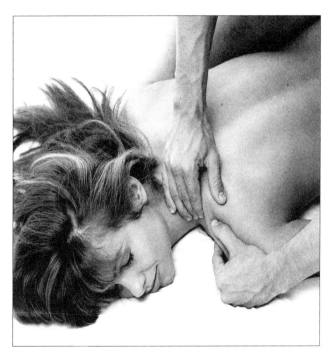

The next stage is picking up (page 57). Begin with the neck, using one hand, working up from the base of the neck to the hairline and indeed into the hair. Be particularly careful not to pinch. Then you can use both hands to work symmetrically, picking up the flesh of the shoulders on both sides. Begin close in to the neck, and work outwards towards the shoulders. Pick up as large an area as you conveniently can, but again, take care not to pinch. Remember to use a rolling wrist action, with the hand moving from a pointing-downwards position to one

lightest possible movement to the nape of the neck; at the end, let your hands leave the shoulders on the final outward movement. This is a particularly good way to end an aromatherapy neck massage.

An alternative way to finish is to place your right hand on the left side of the nape of your partner's neck, and to make a feather stroke to the right shoulder. Follow this with a similar stroke with your left hand. This is a form of alternate feather stroking. Either method should leave your partner with relaxed neck and shoulders.

With your partner lying on his or her back, you can do a neck, shoulders and chest massage. Begin by introducing a little oil onto the area around the collar-bones and upper chest, using alternate, gentle strokes.

Next, place your hands so that they are resting just below your partner's collar-bones, with your fingers pointing inwards and slightly downwards. Move your hands outwards in line with the collar-bones, beginning to rotate your hands outwards as you do so; the aim is to move your fingers outwards across the upper part of the arm, with the

palm of your hand on the point of the shoulder. The palm and ball of the hand is the pivot point, and it is through this point that the main pressure of the move is exerted. The point of maximum pressure is when the palm is on the point of the shoulder: you are, in effect, pressing the shoulders backwards. As soon as you go beyond this point,

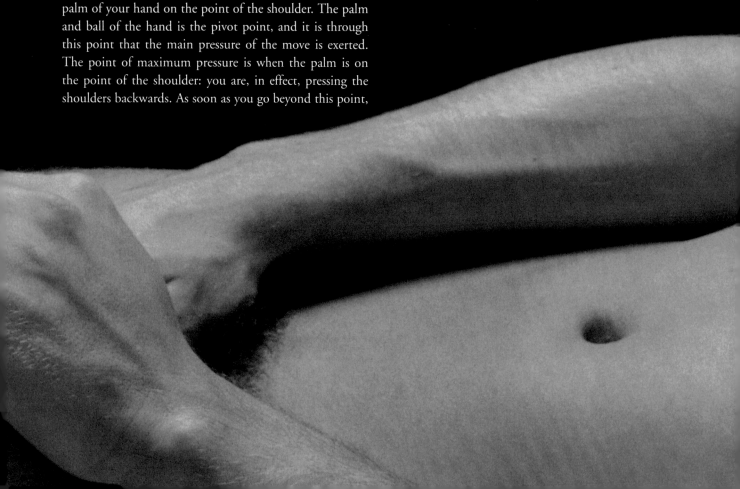

moving your hand still further around the shoulder, and indeed moving it so that it is under the shoulder, the pressure naturally reduces. Mould your hand around your partner's shoulder as you move it towards the back.

You should now be very lightly supporting your partner's shoulders from underneath, with your thumbs pointing outwards, and your fingers pointing inwards. Next, you move your fingertips up beside the spine, massaging as you go, exerting the main pressure through the gentle rotation of the tips of your index and middle fingers. You should end up with your fingers at the base of the skull, pointing towards the top of your partner's head. You are now well placed to massage the shiatsu pressure points on the back of the head, just below the bony part of the skull; vibrate your fingertips slightly for a really sensuous massage.

Finally, you can follow the curve of the shoulders outwards, around, and back to the original starting position. Remember to keep your hands in contact with your partner's skin throughout the movement.

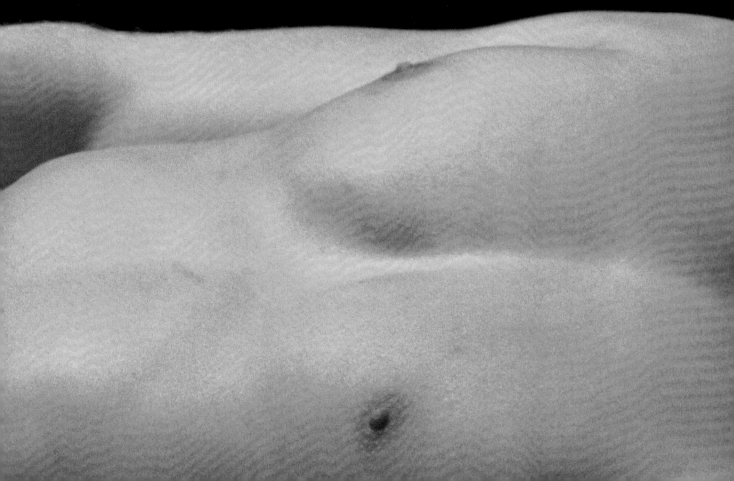

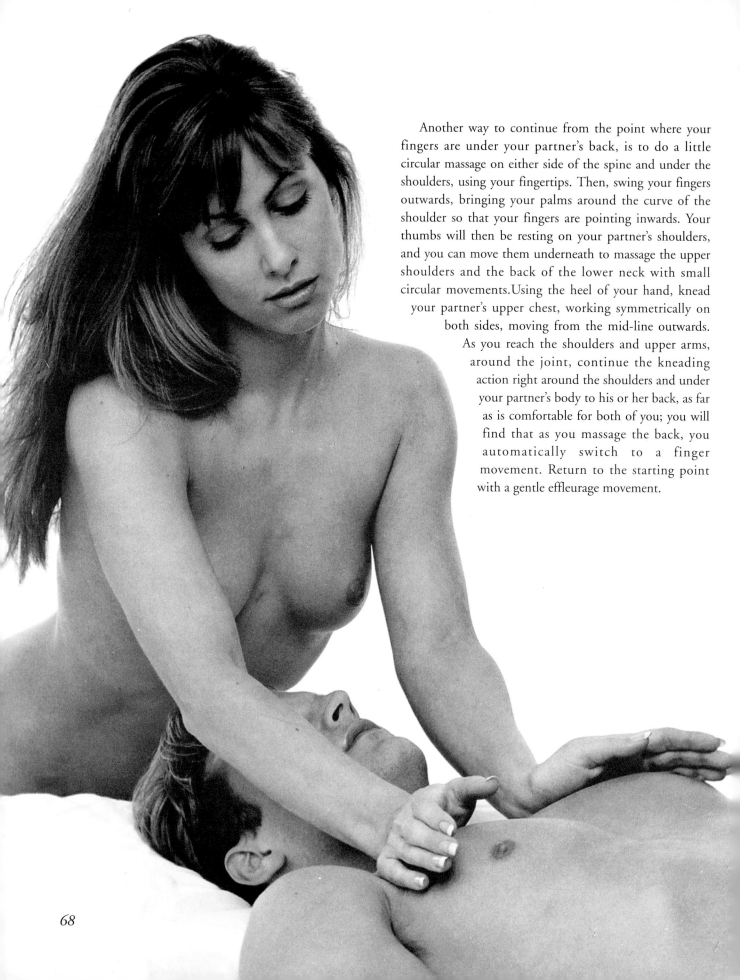

Another way to continue from the point where your fingers are under your partner's back, is to do a little circular massage on either side of the spine and under the shoulders, using your fingertips. Then, swing your fingers outwards, bringing your palms around the curve of the shoulder so that your fingers are pointing inwards. Your thumbs will then be resting on your partner's shoulders, and you can move them underneath to massage the upper shoulders and the back of the lower neck with small circular movements. Using the heel of your hand, knead your partner's upper chest, working symmetrically on both sides, moving from the mid-line outwards. As you reach the shoulders and upper arms, around the joint, continue the kneading action right around the shoulders and under your partner's body to his or her back, as far as is comfortable for both of you; you will find that as you massage the back, you automatically switch to a finger movement. Return to the starting point with a gentle effleurage movement.

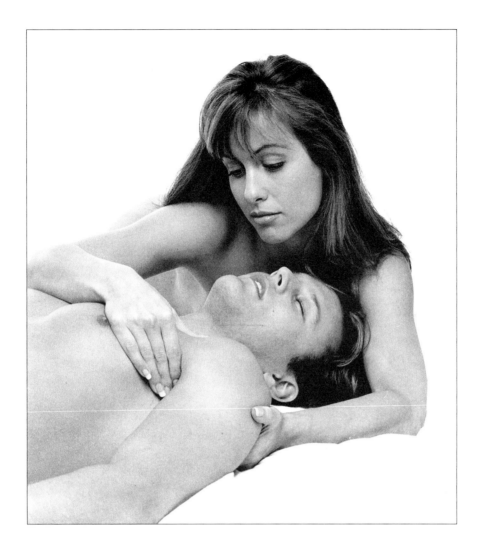

Work on the pectoral muscles between the chest and the armpit with picking-up movements, as illustrated above, kneading, or wringing — whatever feels best. To get your hand in the right position, place the heel of your hand in your partner's armpit, with the palm against the inner surface of their arm: your fingers should point downwards, towards the ground. Use your left hand to massage your partner's right pectorals, and your right for their left. Do one side at a time.

Rotate your hand in the armpit until the pectoral muscle is between your thumb and the rest of your hand; this is the part you pick up, repeatedly, taking care not to pinch your partner.

To complete a neck and shoulders massage, stroke your partner gently with side strokes to the neck, starting with one hand on each side of the neck and stroking alternately from the shoulders to the base of the skull. A good alternative is side strokes to the neck and shoulders: taking each side in turn, use both hands alternately, again stroking from the shoulders to the base of the neck. Finally, place one hand on each side of the shoulders; run the hands over the shoulders to the base of the neck; support the head gently around the ears; and lean gently backwards to exert a very gentle pull on the head. Relax the pull and release the head, sliding your hands slowly and gently upwards past the crown of the head.

BACK MASSAGE

MOST OF US do not pay much attention to our backs, except when they hurt; and certainly we pay very little attention to the sensuous qualities of the back. And yet, the back can repay massage — especially sensuous massage — very generously. Sometimes it seems as if half the tensions of our lives are stored in our backs, and a good massage can melt them away; and if we allow ourselves to stop being distracted for a while by the everyday concerns of life, we can discover unexpected reserves of sensuality in that broad, smooth area of skin.

After spreading the massage medium with gentle, alternate effleurage strokes, you begin the effleurage in earnest. The basic procedure is simple enough. Working symmetrically with both hands, from the lower part of the back, you go up the middle of the back on either side of the spine, returning with a light pressure on the linking stroke; repeat about three times. Next, you move outwards slightly, and repeat the motion. The main pressure, of course, is on the up stroke. Again, you do this about three times. Finally, you move a little further out again, and move up the side of the body; the movement stops naturally at the armpits, so you have to make a modest effort to maintain the smooth, easy flow of the return movement.

Kneading, either symmetrically or in alternate strokes, follows. Now, you are applying rather greater force, rhythmically increasing and decreasing the pressure through the heel of the hand. Work from bottom to top, linking the strokes with effleurage return movements. As with the effleurage already described, work near the spine first; then further out; and finally on the sides, repeating each movement three or four times. You can exert additional force by using both hands together, one on top of the other, and working on one side at a time. Once you have done this, you can if you wish incorporate a neck and shoulder massage, as already described, for which your partner needs to rest his or her forehead on folded hands, so that their neck is straight and relaxed.

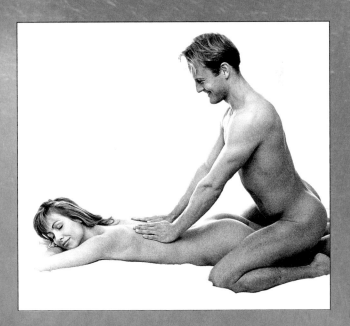 

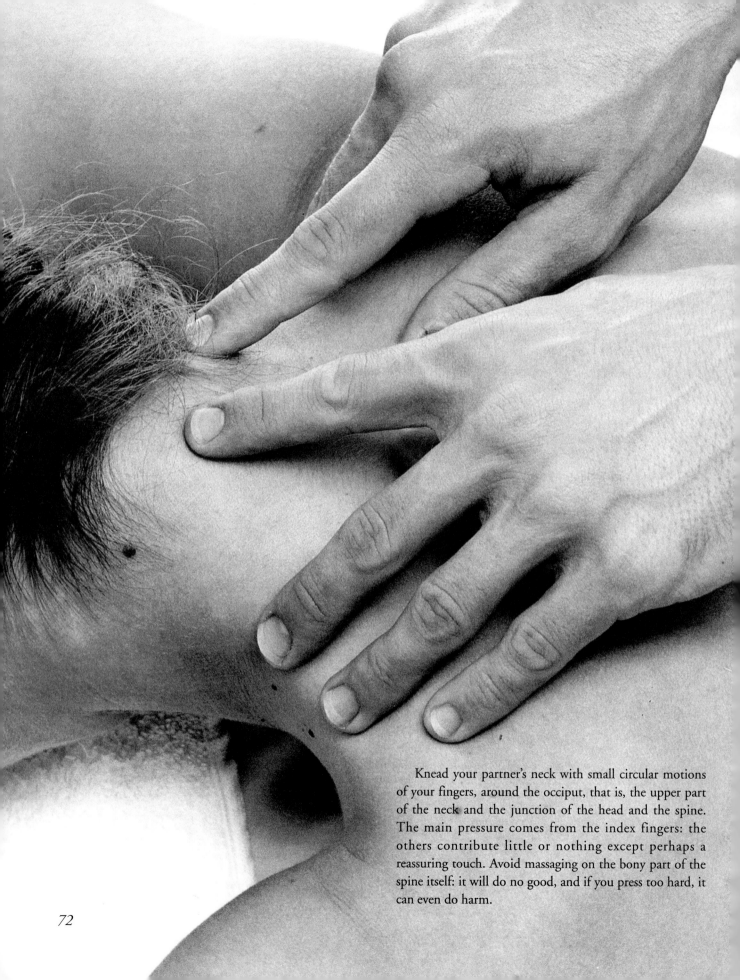

Knead your partner's neck with small circular motions of your fingers, around the occiput, that is, the upper part of the neck and the junction of the head and the spine. The main pressure comes from the index fingers: the others contribute little or nothing except perhaps a reassuring touch. Avoid massaging on the bony part of the spine itself: it will do no good, and if you press too hard, it can even do harm.

Gradually work your way down the neck and the back, feeling with your fingers for knots and stiff muscles. This is very satisfying for both partners: when you find and release a knot of tension, both partners feel a sense of release. Although the actual process of unravelling a knot can be painful, it is definitely on the borderline between pleasure and pain; and when the knot is gone, only the pleasure is left.

As well as using your fingers, you can switch to using the pads of your thumbs, either for extra, broader pressure or simply because your fingers are getting tired. Using your thumbs is particularly useful towards the lower back, though another technique is to go one way (top to bottom, say) using the fingers, then go back the other way using your thumbs. This provides a welcome variation in feel and pressure for both parties.

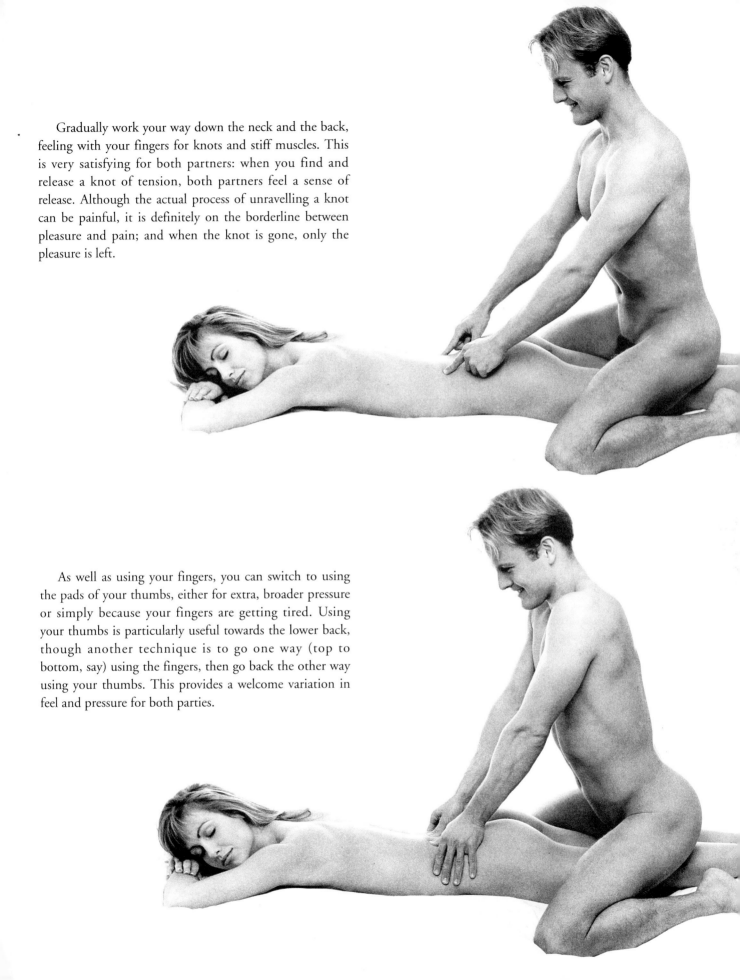

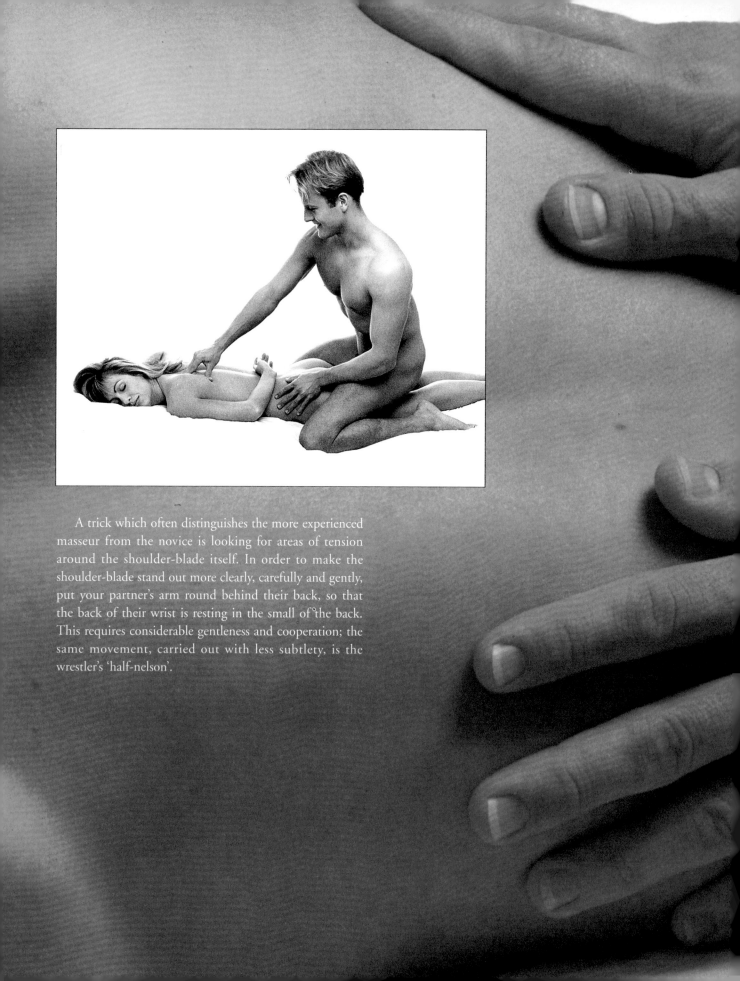

A trick which often distinguishes the more experienced masseur from the novice is looking for areas of tension around the shoulder-blade itself. In order to make the shoulder-blade stand out more clearly, carefully and gently, put your partner's arm round behind their back, so that the back of their wrist is resting in the small of the back. This requires considerable gentleness and cooperation; the same movement, carried out with less subtlety, is the wrestler's 'half-nelson'.

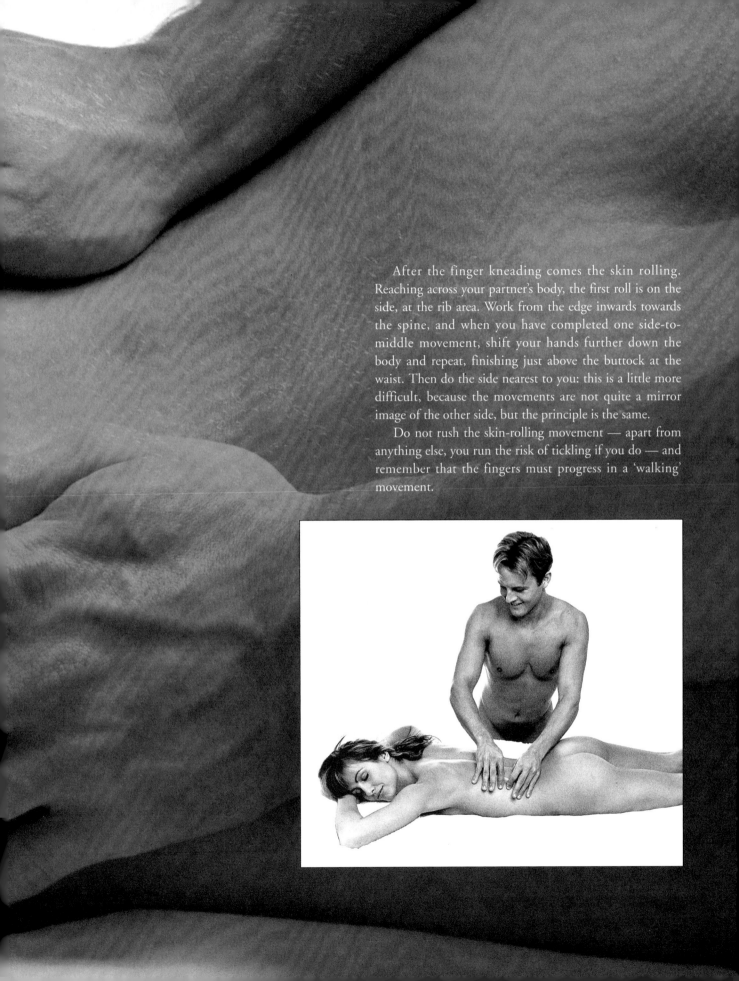

After the finger kneading comes the skin rolling. Reaching across your partner's body, the first roll is on the side, at the rib area. Work from the edge inwards towards the spine, and when you have completed one side-to-middle movement, shift your hands further down the body and repeat, finishing just above the buttock at the waist. Then do the side nearest to you: this is a little more difficult, because the movements are not quite a mirror image of the other side, but the principle is the same.

Do not rush the skin-rolling movement — apart from anything else, you run the risk of tickling if you do — and remember that the fingers must progress in a 'walking' movement.

Wringing follows on from skin rolling. Start in much the same place as for the skin rolling, though obviously you will be manipulating rather larger areas of flesh with each movement, and wring back and forth towards and away from the spine; you do not however 'walk' in towards the spine as you do with skin rolling. Work steadily down the body, then back up again; you can repeat this several times. Then you come in closer to the spine, and wring the flesh of the back and sides, rather than just the sides. Then do the other side of your partner's body.

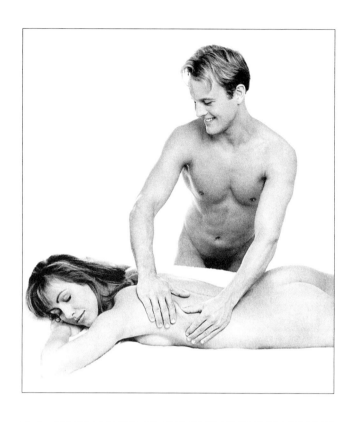

Cupping and hacking require little explanation, as they have been illustrated for the back on pages 59 and 60. Begin at the outer edge of the back, and work downwards. The most important thing, which cannot be over-emphasized, is to avoid the kidney area. 'Jump over' it as you work from the top of the back down to the buttocks and back up again. After you have massaged the outer edge of the back, move in a little and repeat each movement; avoid both the kidneys, and direct contact with the spine.

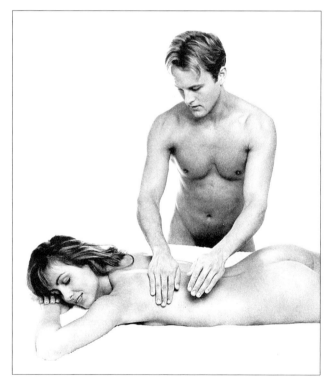

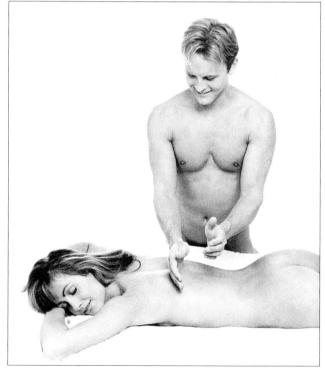

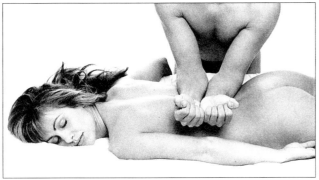

After the cupping and hacking, refresh the back with symmetrical effleurage strokes, and finish by applying deep, spine-stretching effleurage with the forearms as illustrated. This is definitely not a percussion stroke. Place the backs of the forearms in the middle of your partner's back, with your fists clenched, and move your arms outwards, one towards their head and one towards their feet. You do not want to exert a great deal of pressure, but you must exert enough to create a satisfactory stretching movement along the spine.

Alternatively (or afterwards), you can make ever-lighter 'cat strokes' first with your hands, then your fingers, then your fingertips, working from the shoulders downwards and decreasing the pressure until you are not touching your partner at all.

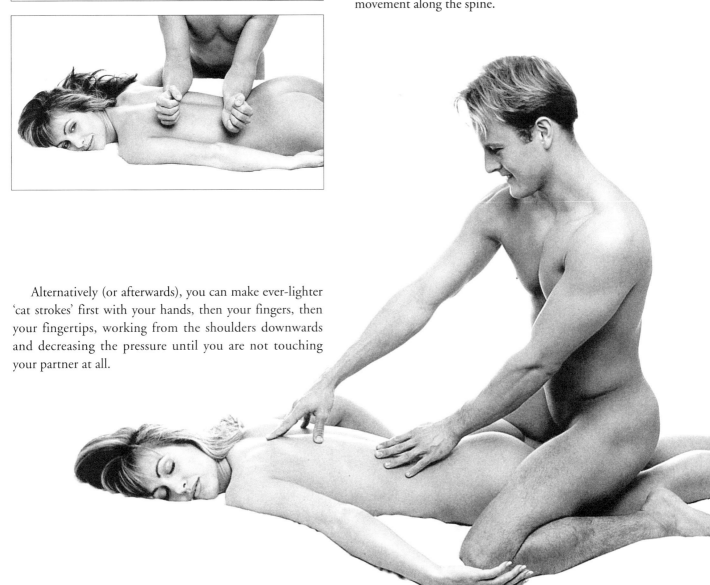

HEAD AND FACE

STRICTLY SPEAKING, a head and face massage should not fall between a back massage and a foot massage, as it does here: the normal sequence for a full body massage is right leg; left leg; left arm; chest and neck; right arm; abdomen; back and buttocks. The face would be a separate massage at the end. On the other hand, although we would always recommend a full body massage in this sequence, we are aware that some people may lack either the time or the inclination to do things this way; and because a head and face massage brings quick and welcome benefits in a self-contained package, we have elected to put things in the order in which you find them here.

At its most basic, just stroking someone's head is soothing and stress relieving; but if you apply a logical massage sequence, a head and face massage will be much more effective. When you have finished, you may be surprised at how much younger your partner looks. This is as true for men as for women, though a fresh shave is a good idea.

The simplest (and most effective) movement is stroking, but more than in any other massage, the movements should flow smoothly from one to another, and the hands should mould to the skin, in the words of one masseur, 'like silk cloth'. You must be particularly careful in your choice of oils — nothing too pungent, and use it sparingly — and you may care to add wheat germ oil which is high in vitamin E and is therefore particularly good for the skin.

Begin with your partner lying on his or her back, with the head towards you. Place your hands at the base of the neck, or even on the chest, and sweep them up to the chin. Pause momentarily, with the chin in the 'V' formed by your fingers, then continue to stroke upwards and outwards under the jaw, towards the ears. Pause again when your fingers are at your partner's ears, then gently return them back under the chin.

With your fingers, stroke symmetrically up around the bottom of the lips — try not to touch the lips accidentally — and upwards and outwards in a 'smile', continuing the stroke up and outwards towards the cheek-bones. Follow the line of the cheek-bones to the temples, gradually slowing the movement and increasing the pressure slightly. Hold the pressure for a moment at the temples, then glide the fingers back to beneath the chin.

Next, stroke upwards but stay closer in: the effleurage moves up beside the nose to the bridge, then the fingers move apart and outwards across the forehead to the temples. Then they return to the chin, as before. Repeat this sequence, from the very beginning, two or three times.

Use both hands together, with one thumb resting on the other: this helps to equalize the pressure on both sides of the face. Moving around the mouth, make small circular movements with your fingers; the pressure should be greater on the upward curve, and less on the downward part of the movement. Do this for half a minute or more.

Next, stroke with your fingertips from the upper lip to the cheeks, like the painted moustache of a toy soldier. Continue the movement all the way to the temples. Then make a similar movement, starting under the mouth, but again going up the cheeks to the temples. As before, slow the movement and increase the pressure slightly as you reach the temples.

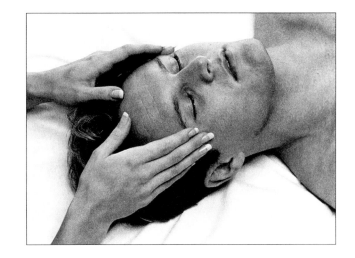

Finally, working on each cheek in turn, 'roll' the fingers of one hand and then the other on the cheek-bone. This 'rolling' movement is hard to show in a picture, but what you are doing is to touch down first with your index finger, then the middle finger, then (as the index finger leaves) the ring finger, and finally the little finger. Repeat several times before doing the other cheek. The same stroke is also very pleasant on the forehead, beginning at the centre, working slowly to one side, then returning to the centre and working over to the other side. Stroking the neck can be done either before or after a cheek massage, whichever you prefer. It is very simple. You work on one side of the neck at a time. With one hand, stroke firmly but gently up from the front of the neck, around the jaw line, and up to the ear. Lift the hand off at the ear, and follow the same motion with the other hand. Repeat several times with a continuous flowing motion, then do the same on the other side.

Eye massage must be very gentle indeed; normally, you try not to touch the eyes themselves at all. Place the fingertips of your hands on your partner's eyebrows, and stroke just above the eyebrow with your index and middle finger or middle and ring finger, moving out towards the temples. Follow the socket of the eye around, bringing your fingers to the bridge of the nose. Repeat up to half a dozen times. Finally, run your index and middle fingers on either side of your partner's eyebrows, starting at the middle and working outwards, ending the stroke at the temples with a gentle pressure.

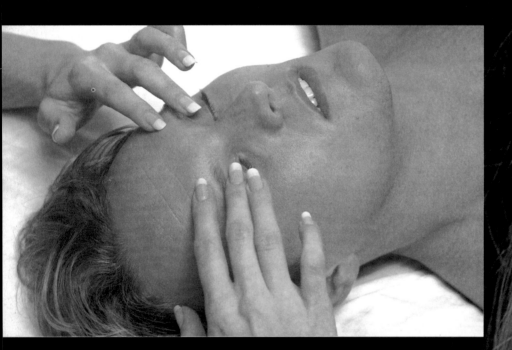

There are four shiatsu points around the eyes, roughly on the points of a cross: imagine someone wearing clown make-up. The first point is just where the bridge of the nose broadens into the eyebrows; the second is directly above the middle of the eye, just at the bottom of the eyebrow, on the bone of the skull; the third is at the outer end of the eyebrow ridge; and the fourth is on the bone of the eye socket, just about directly beneath the second point. Use very light pressure with the pads of the index fingers on all of these.

To massage your partner's forehead place your hands, one on each side, with the tips of the fingers just interlocking. Move your fingers apart, exerting a light but steady pressure as you move towards the temples; the movement is as if you were very gently stretching the skin of the forehead, though you should not really be pulling at all. This is a series of movements that start from the middle of the forehead. The movements should be small at first, gradually getting larger and moving further out towards the temples each time.

Move the fingers back towards the centre each time in the same path, but with hardly any pressure. When you reach the temples, pause for a moment with a very gentle pressure.

As the forehead holds an enormous amount of tension, further time spent easing the frown-lines away will be well rewarded.

With your hands on your partner's cheeks and temples, and your thumbs on the bridge of their nose, stroke outwards with your thumbs just above the eyebrows. Repeat, a little higher each time, until you reach the hair line. Finally, make small circular movements with your thumbs or fingers, all over the forehead, working outwards from the centre.

To give your partner a scalp massage, begin at the front of the head and make small circles with the pads of your fingers.

Move all over the scalp, maintaining a gentle, constant rotary motion, not forgetting the hollows at the back of the skull, which often seem to be the most tense areas.

The last part of a head and face massage is a neck stretch. This should not be a violent pull, but a very gentle, steady one. Cradle the head, with your grip well down towards the neck: only your little fingers should actually be resting on the skull. Exert a steady, gentle pressure for a few seconds, then move your hands so that they are on either side of your partner's head. Hold their head for a few moments more, then gently slide your hands up and beyond the crown of the head. You may care to repeat this a couple of times, slowly.

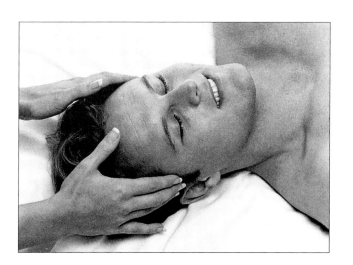

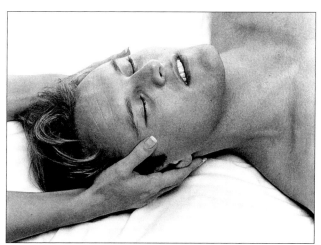

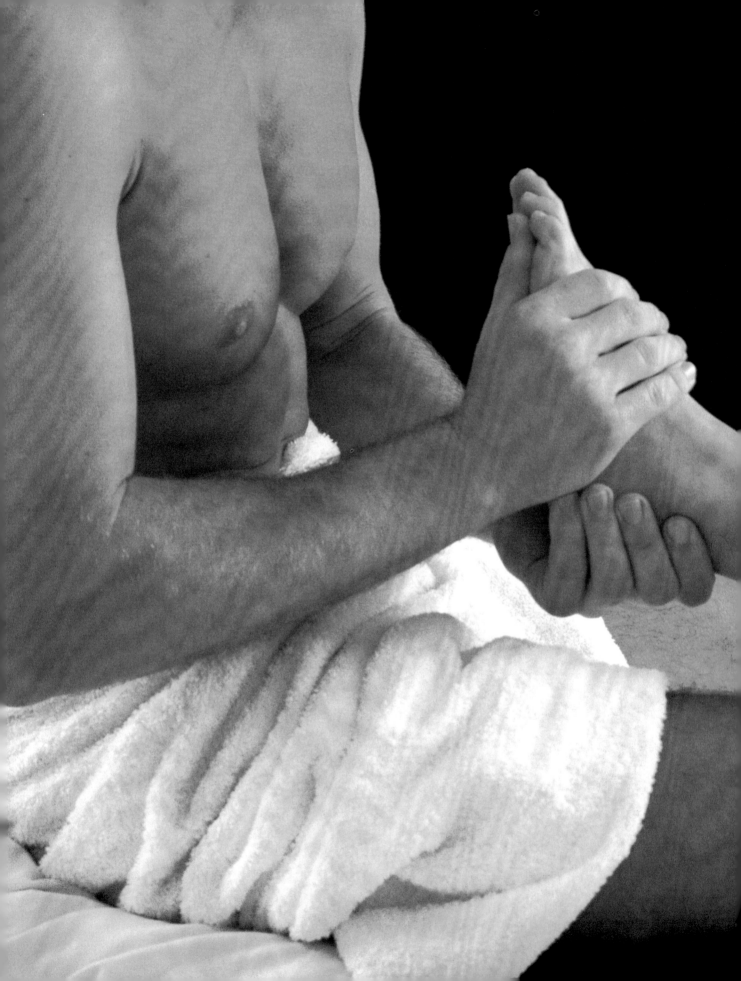

FOOT MASSAGE

FEET HAVE A HARD LIFE. Incredibly complex engineering structures, with 28 bones and countless nerve endings, they bear the body's whole weight and are normally shut up in leather boxes all day. They receive next to no love and attention from most people; no wonder they complain.

And yet, they repay massage more than almost any other part of the body, with deep reserves of sensuousness as a bonus. Tired feet communicate their unhappiness to the whole of the body; and happy feet communicate their joy.

The techniques for massaging the top of the foot and the sole are quite different. The thick skin on the sole requires firm pressure, but the many delicate bones of the upper part require a gentler touch. If you or your partner is troubled with ticklish feet, it is worth knowing that a massage elsewhere — especially the leg — may remove the problem, so that you can return to the feet later. Using a minimum of oil, which is all you need anyway, also reduces the risk of ticklishness.

The techniques used are various forms of stroking, thumb pressure and knuckling. Some people use percussion techniques, but we feel that these are inappropriate to the foot, especially in a sensual massage. As well as the massage movements, you can exercise the foot by supporting the ankle with one hand and gently flexing the foot up and down, taking it to the limit of its comfortable movement. Then turn it from side to side, and finish by rotating it several times in each direction. This is normally done towards the end of the massage.

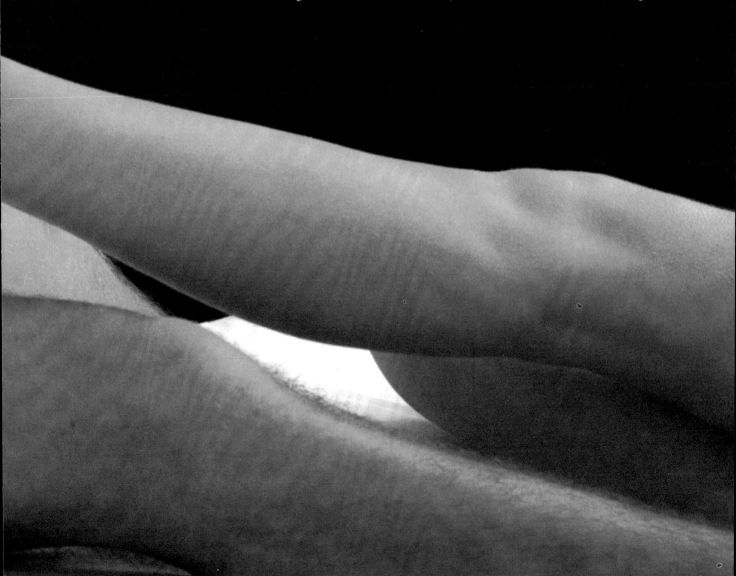

Begin by stroking the foot, starting with your hands at the toes, one above the foot and the other below. Stroke the hands firmly down to the heel and ankle.

When you reach the end of the stroke, rotate your hands so that your palms are towards the toes, and return with a lighter stroke. Do this four times (or more), maintaining a smooth, continuous flow from one movement to the next.

Next move on to thumb stroking. Hold your partner's foot with your fingers under the ball of the foot, and your thumbs resting naturally on the top, at the base of the toes. Exerting a gentle pressure, push your thumbs up towards the top of the foot, moving them gently outwards in a fan movement as you do so. Repeat four or five times.

Now go back to the rest position, and move the thumbs alternately in the same way, using longer strokes and carrying the stroke round to the side of the foot and the ankle. Towards the end of the stroke, your whole hand

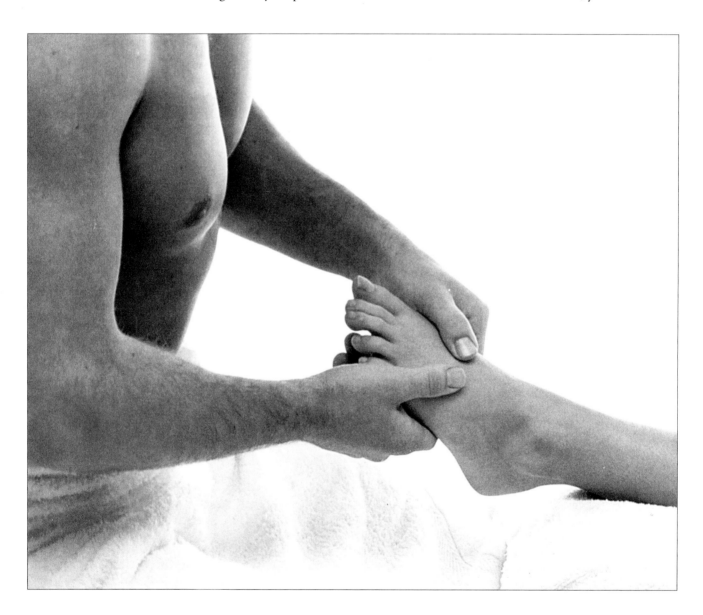

should move as you use the heel of the thumb to apply pressure. Again, do this four or five times. Go back to the rest position again, but instead of the fan-like strokes, gently seek out the depressions between the tendons of the toes and stroke upwards, away from the base of the toes, using the thumbs alternately to follow each depression in turn until it peters out.

Applying pressure to the ball of the foot begins almost as a mirror image of the previous stroke, with the fingers on top of the foot and the thumbs resting just below the ball of the foot. Press firmly with the thumbs, 'rolling' the pressure under the pad of the thumb but without moving the whole thumb.

After a few seconds, move the thumbs a very small distance and repeat, until you have massaged the whole of the ball of the foot, paying especial attention to the area under the big toe. Then work slowly downwards, until you have massaged the whole of the sole.

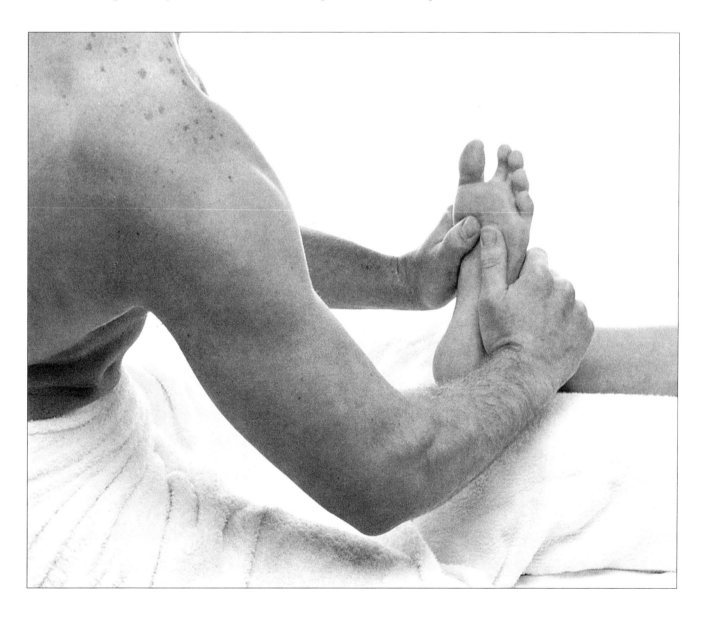

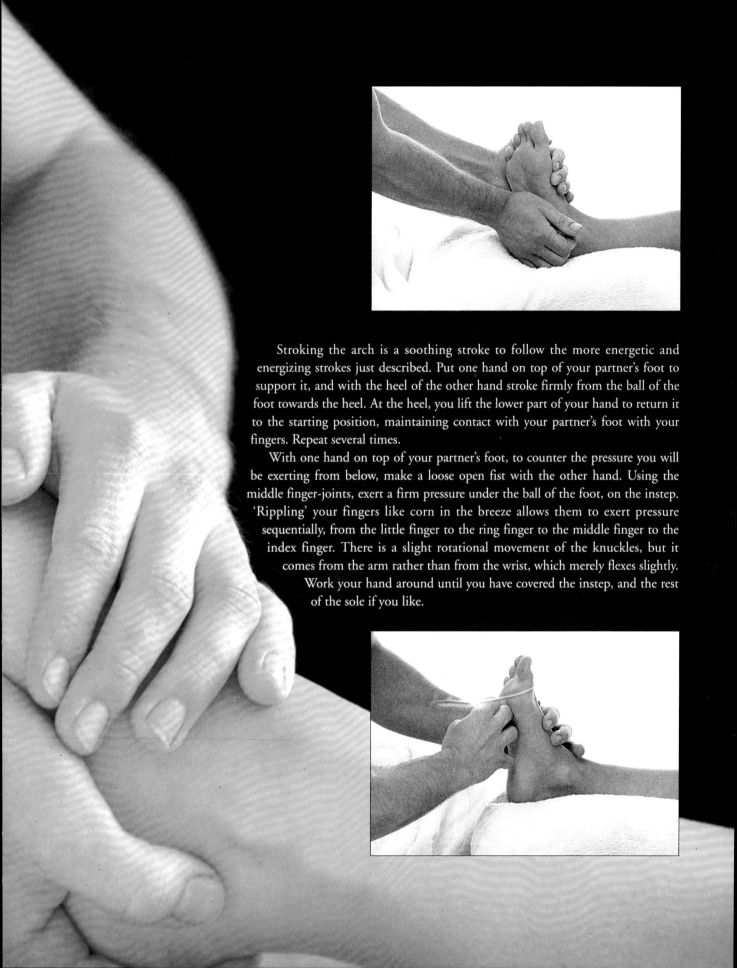

Stroking the arch is a soothing stroke to follow the more energetic and energizing strokes just described. Put one hand on top of your partner's foot to support it, and with the heel of the other hand stroke firmly from the ball of the foot towards the heel. At the heel, you lift the lower part of your hand to return it to the starting position, maintaining contact with your partner's foot with your fingers. Repeat several times.

With one hand on top of your partner's foot, to counter the pressure you will be exerting from below, make a loose open fist with the other hand. Using the middle finger-joints, exert a firm pressure under the ball of the foot, on the instep. 'Rippling' your fingers like corn in the breeze allows them to exert pressure sequentially, from the little finger to the ring finger to the middle finger to the index finger. There is a slight rotational movement of the knuckles, but it comes from the arm rather than from the wrist, which merely flexes slightly.

Work your hand around until you have covered the instep, and the rest of the sole if you like.

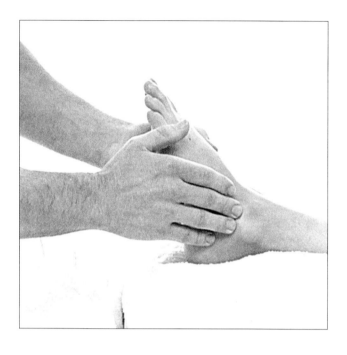

With one hand on either side of the ankle, make small rotary kneading movements with your fingers on both sides. Make these little circles all around the ankle, with more pressure on the upward stroke than on the downward stroke.

Cup the ball of the foot in one hand, so that your partner's toes rest on the ball of your hand. Place your other hand on top, and move your hands in a kneading motion on either side of the foot. This wiggles, warms and relaxes the toes.

You can also hold the foot with one hand, and enfold your partners toes in your other hand, again flexing them to and fro — gently!

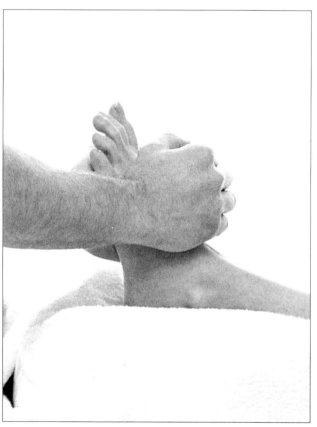

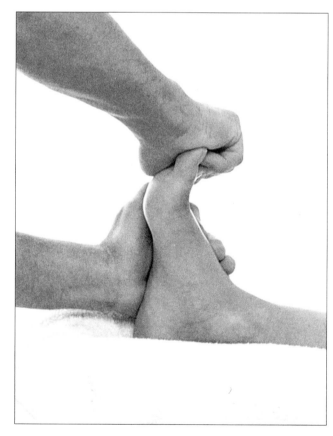

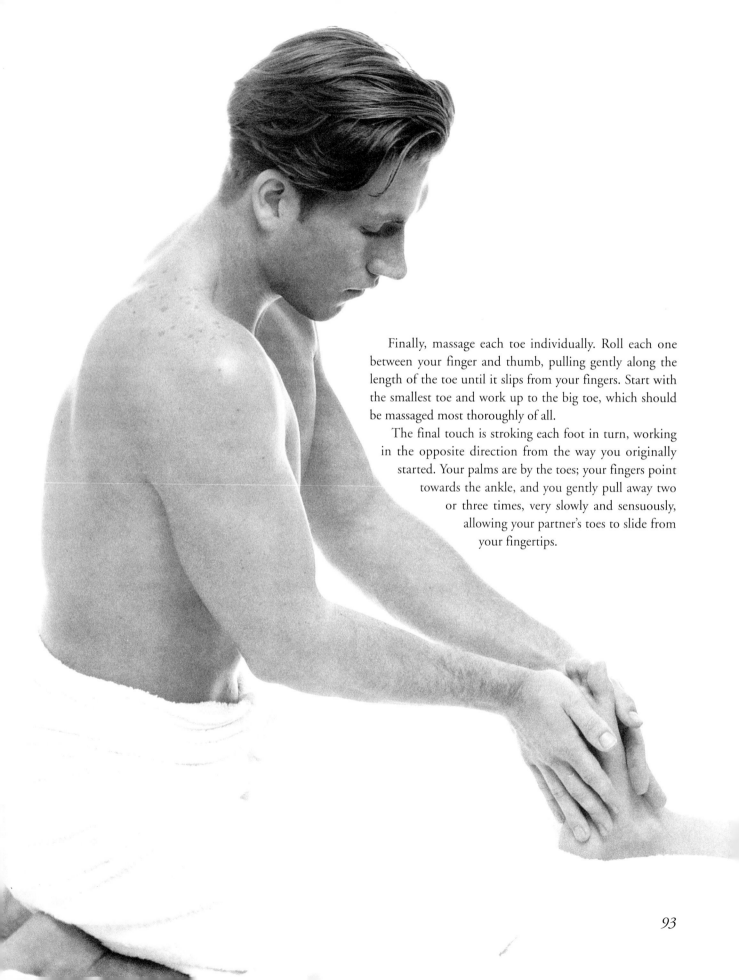

Finally, massage each toe individually. Roll each one between your finger and thumb, pulling gently along the length of the toe until it slips from your fingers. Start with the smallest toe and work up to the big toe, which should be massaged most thoroughly of all.

The final touch is stroking each foot in turn, working in the opposite direction from the way you originally started. Your palms are by the toes; your fingers point towards the ankle, and you gently pull away two or three times, very slowly and sensuously, allowing your partner's toes to slide from your fingertips.

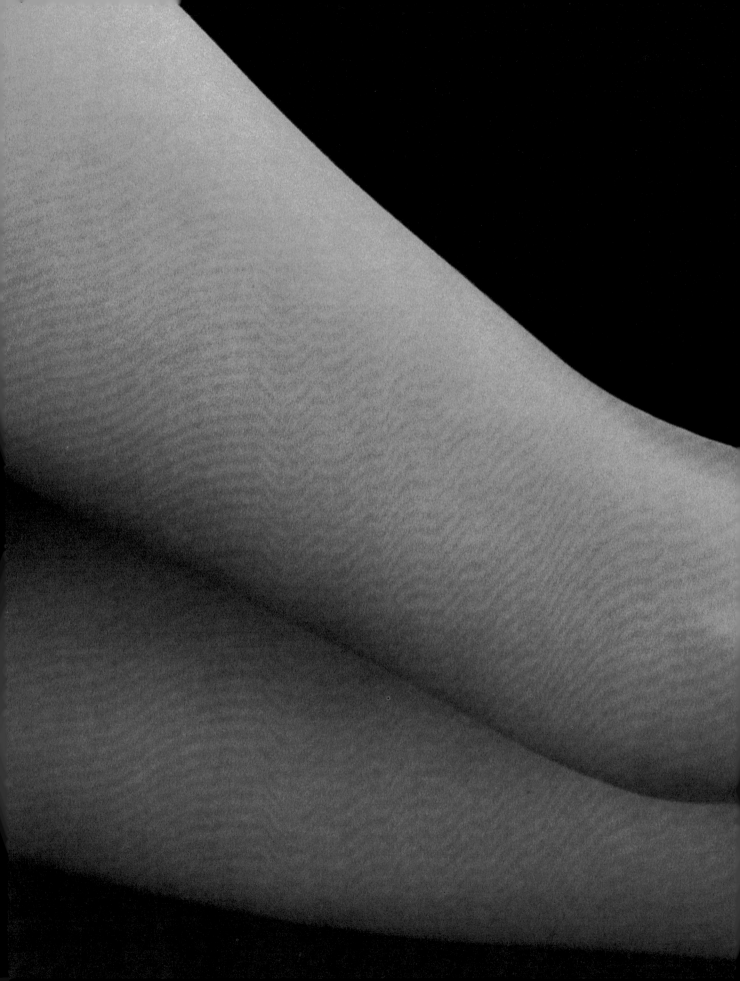

LEG MASSAGE

FOR SOME PEOPLE, a leg massage is the most sensual of all. The leg is a complex pillar of muscle and bone, which supports our weight except when we are sitting or lying down; and whether we have been standing still, or walking or running long distances, our legs get tired. For that matter, leg massage is arguably even more important for someone who leads a sedentary life-style: it helps to keep the muscles toned, and improves the circulation. The legs are sometimes known as 'the second heart', because of the contribution they make to the circulation of the blood.

You should begin the massage, after the usual application of massage medium, by gentle effleurage starting with the foot. A foot massage is not a part of a leg massage (though the two go naturally together in a whole-body massage).

Hold the foot between your hands as shown, and slide your hands all the way up the top surface of your partner's leg in a firm effleurage movement. As you get to the top of the leg, swing your fingers inwards towards each other, going into the groin.

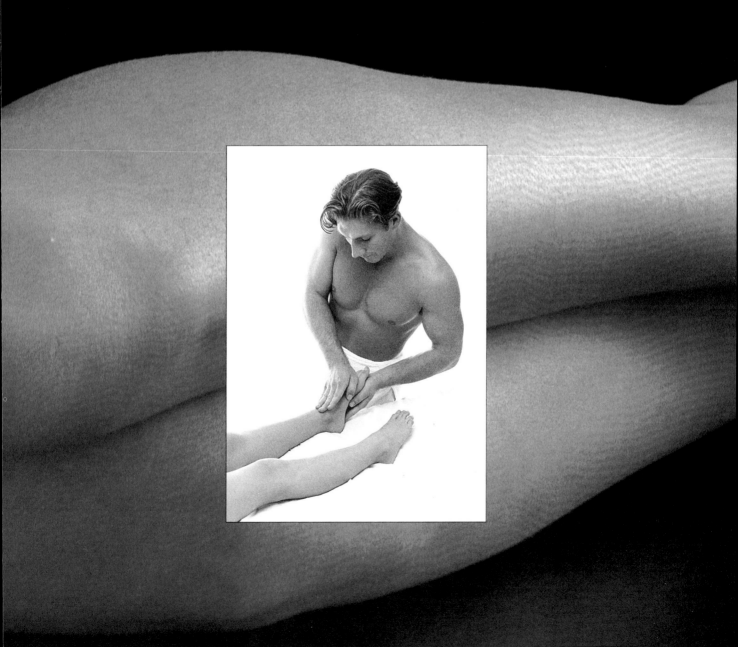

At the groin, gently release the pressure and return to the starting point with a smooth, continuous light effleurage. Repeat this a couple of times (or more).

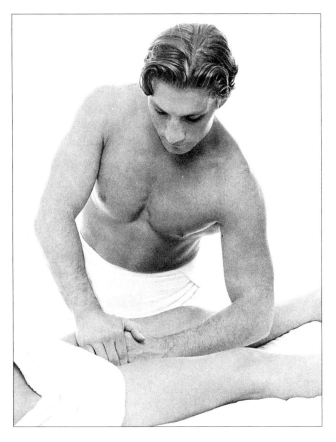

Next, make a similar deep effleurage movement up the leg, but on the sides rather than on the top. Make the same kind of turn at the upper thigh as you previously made at the groin. Again, repeat as often as you wish.

The third deep effleurage is, unsurprisingly, along the back of the leg, which you will have to lift slightly as you move your hands up it. You will find that the knee lifts pretty much of its own accord. At the top of the stroke, on the thigh, you slide your hands around to the top in the same way that you did before, and again return with gentler effleurage. Repeat.

Kneading comes next. First you work on the upper part of the leg, above the knee, making circular kneading movements with the heels of your hands. On the upper surface, your hands work side by side, making alternate strokes. When you knead the sides, you use one hand to provide a counter pressure, holding the leg still and kneading with the other hand. When you massage the underside, you again make kneading motions with both hands, moving alternately, but with one hand on top and one hand underneath. As usual, there is more pressure on the upward part of the circular motion than on the downward part, where all you need is light contact. Finish each kneading movement with effleurage up to the groin. After kneading, pick up the flesh on the inside of the thigh (see page 57), then on the outside; on the top, pick up using a double-handed movement.

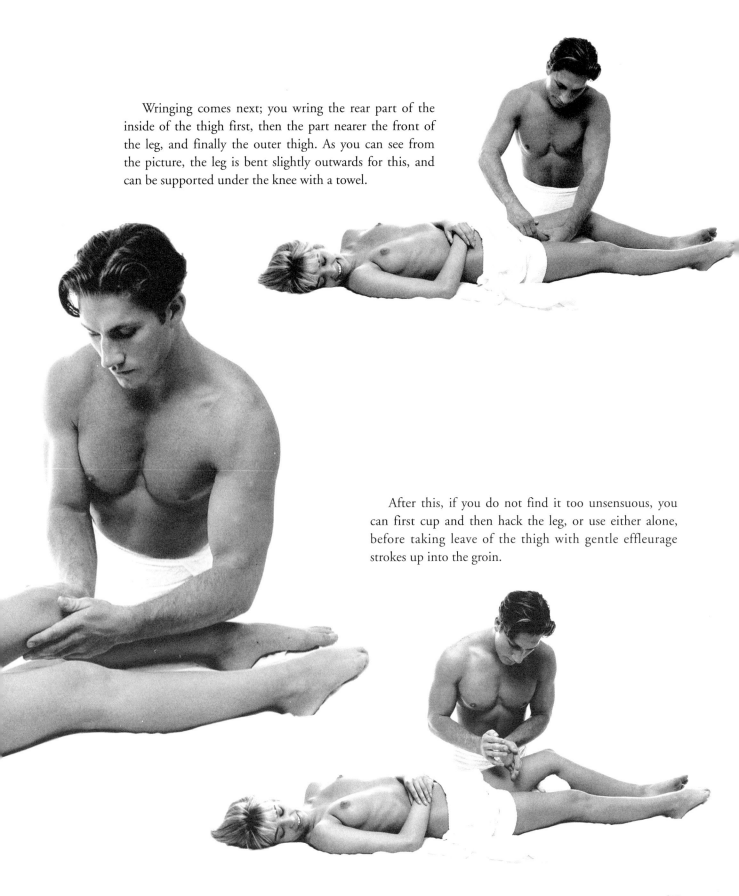

Wringing comes next; you wring the rear part of the inside of the thigh first, then the part nearer the front of the leg, and finally the outer thigh. As you can see from the picture, the leg is bent slightly outwards for this, and can be supported under the knee with a towel.

After this, if you do not find it too unsensuous, you can first cup and then hack the leg, or use either alone, before taking leave of the thigh with gentle effleurage strokes up into the groin.

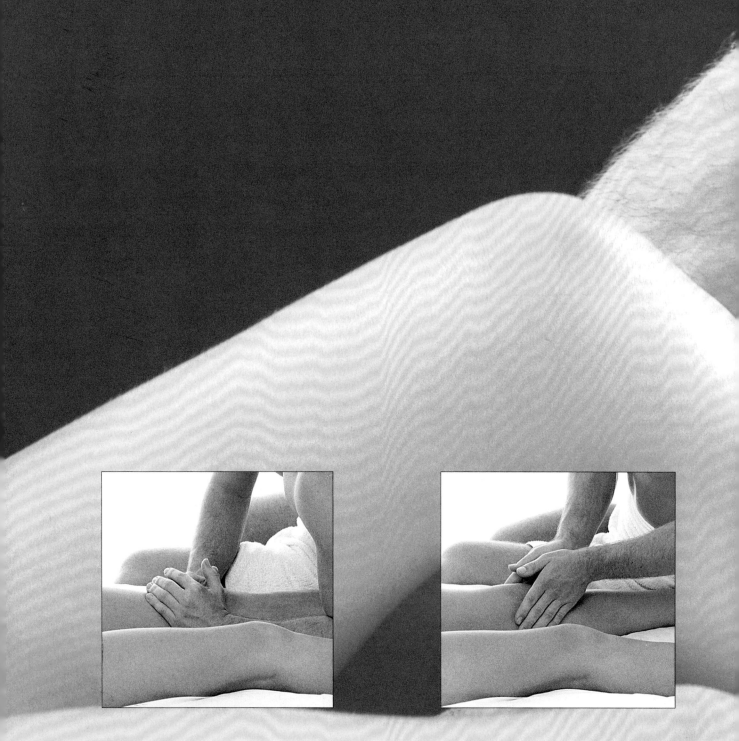

Massaging the knee begins with your hands cradling around the kneecap; your thumbs should be just above the kneecap. Now, you simultaneously make a circular motion — almost as if you were moulding a sand-castle or a mud pie — and you rotate your wrist so that your fingers move downwards.

You should end up with your fingers below the knee and on either side of the leg, as shown in the second picture. Then, leaving your fingertips where they are, push towards the back of the leg and also very slightly towards the upper part of the leg; your hands will move at about forty-five degrees to both the leg and the massage table or

floor. What you are aiming at is the back of the knee; you should end up with your fingertips close to the hollow behind the knee, as shown in the third picture. It would be all but impossible to explain this movement without illustrations!

To return, rotate your hands around your wrists so that the fingers are uppermost, and move them upwards towards the kneecap so that you are back where you started. Repeat twice.

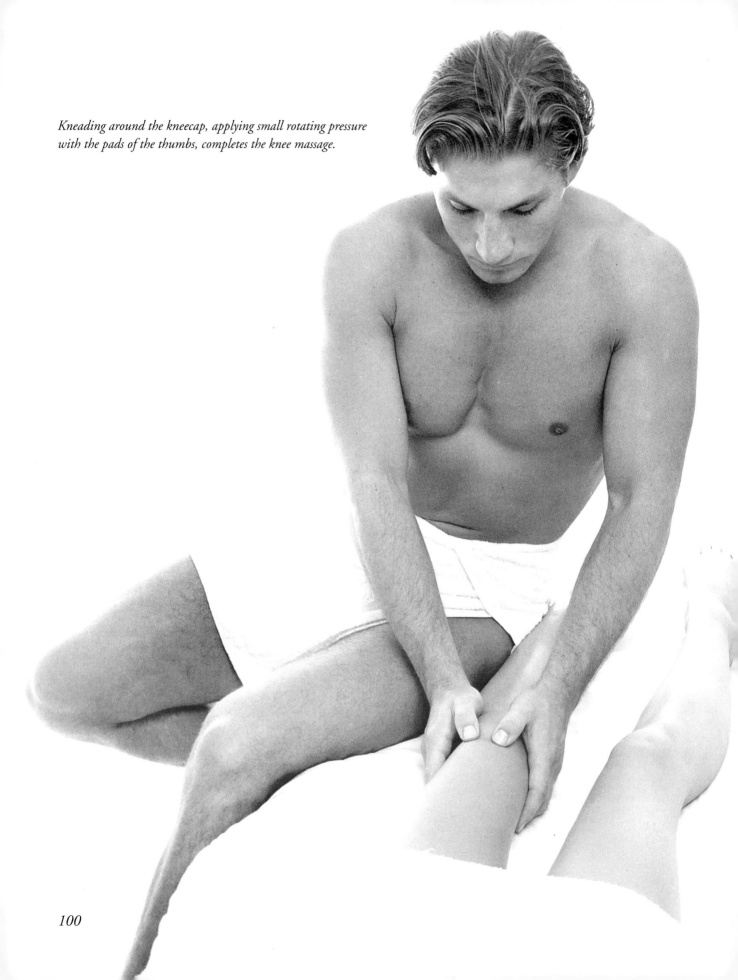

Kneading around the kneecap, applying small rotating pressure with the pads of the thumbs, completes the knee massage.

100

After finishing with the knee, use effleurage strokes down to the toes; then if you need to, spread a little more oil on the lower leg. With your partner's knees still turned out slightly, knead the calf muscles; pick them up; then wring them. These are absolutely straightforward massage strokes. You can also hack if you wish, though this is a bit too hearty to qualify as 'sensual' in some people's eyes. Knead the bony part at the front of the lower leg with your thumbs — not with the heels of your hands — beginning at the knee and working down towards the ankle until you lose contact with the bone; the picture shows you how.

At this point, you might decide to do a foot massage; but if you do not, then just stroke off the leg using gentle effleurage or feather strokes, working down to the foot and coming off at the toes.

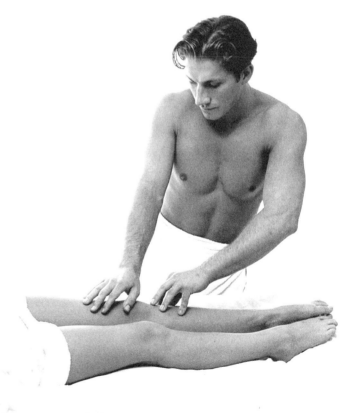

S OME PEOPLE find arm massages much more sensuous than other people, but most find a good hand massage to be very sensuous and relaxing. Like the back and the feet, hands are often one of the most neglected parts of our bodies. And yet, because our fingers are what we rely on for many of our sensations of touch, we can 'tune in' to their needs and to how they feel with remarkable sensitivity.

Another advantage of a hand massage is that it is something you can do without any elaborate preparation, and without undressing at all. You can just sit together with your partner at the end of the day, and exchange hand massages while you unwind. Of course, because your hands are so sensitive and because they are so rarely pampered, there is no telling where a hand massage may lead...

As with so many other forms of massage, you do not need to follow formal massage procedures; we all know the comfort which can come from just holding the hand of a loved one, and the lightening of our cares which can come when they pick up our hand. Indeed, it is advisable not to start a hand massage too soon: spend a long time holding your partner's hand, and maybe caressing it occasionally, before you begin to massage it.

The eyes may be known as the window of the soul, but the hands can be the window of the mood. When you do start to apply massage techniques, they will then be all the more effective.

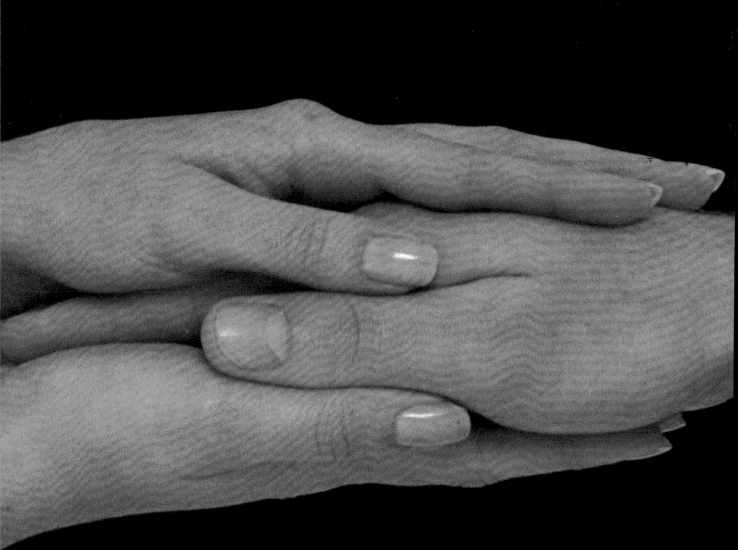

Massage out tiredness in your partner's hand by kneading the palm of their hand with the ball of your hand, pushing fairly firmly down towards the wrist and lightening the pressure considerably on the way back.

Then turn your partner's hand over, and support it with your fingers. This is one of several areas of massage where having someone else support the weight is a luxury in itself; others include the head and the feet. Use the pads of your thumbs to make a fan stroke on the back of the hand, working towards the wrist, either symmetrically or alternately — or try both.

Another way to massage your partner's hand is to support it underneath with one hand, and stroke the back of the hand in much the same way as just described. At the same time, using the supporting hand, pull gently on the index finger; then on the index and middle fingers together; next on the first three fingers; and finally on all four fingers together.

Hold your index, middle and ring fingers together, with the little finger splayed out on each hand. With your partner's palm upwards, interlock your hand with theirs as shown in the picture: their middle three fingers are free, and your middle fingers are supporting their hand. Open your partner's hand, gently, to stretch the palm. The muscles are gently eased into a position which is the very antithesis of the normal grasping movement of the hand, so it counteracts the tension of everyday use.

Use your thumbs to massage the palm of your partner's hand: either both thumbs together in a fanning movement, or just one thumb in small circles. Either way, the aim is a gentle, light kneading. You can afford to be quite firm, but take care to avoid 'digging in'.

Turn the hand over again, so that the palm is down. Support it in your own hands, with your fingers underneath, and gently stroke between each of the tendons of your partner's fingers in turn with the pads of your thumbs, one after the other.

Finally, try a finger massage. Support your partner's hand in your own hand, as shown in the photograph on the left, and massage each of their fingers in turn between your own thumb and forefinger. Roll the finger very slightly to and fro between your own, while gently pulling on it (not hard enough to make it crack!) and letting it slip by; release the fingertip at the end. Repeat several times for each finger, beginning with the little finger and ending with the thumb; you have to turn the hand on its side somewhat in order to be able to massage the base of the thumb properly, using your own thumb. Finish the massage with a couple of palm kneads, before holding your partner's hand between your own for a few seconds as shown on pages 102 and 103 and gently pulling your hands away with a stroking motion on either side. This can be repeated several times.

Arm massage starts with spreading the massage medium in the usual way. Then support your partner's arm under the wrist, and make an effleurage stroke with the other. Begin at the back of the hand, and stroke upwards along the upper side of the arm, tucking your fingers into the armpit as you reach the top and returning with a light effleurage stroke to the starting point; repeat this movement two or three times.

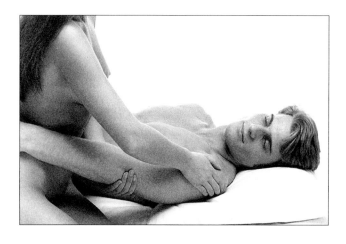

Make a similar stroke up the outside of the arm, past the point of the elbow. When you reach the upper arm, rotate your hand around into the armpit again, and return in the same way as before. Repeat two or three times.

Change hands, so that you are holding your partner's wrist with your other hand, and make another effleurage stroke up the inside of the arm, straight to the armpit. Slide your hand back down the arm, with a light pressure, and return to the starting point. Once again, repeat.

Knead the upper arm with one hand while supporting the elbow with the other. Knead the outside of the arm first, moving up to the shoulder from the elbow; you can also knead the shoulder when you reach it. Return using the usual effleurage strokes.

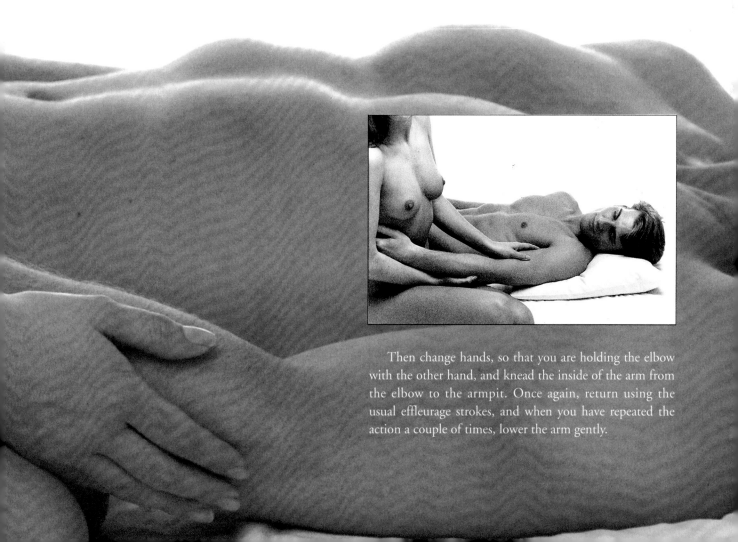

Then change hands, so that you are holding the elbow with the other hand, and knead the inside of the arm from the elbow to the armpit. Once again, return using the usual effleurage strokes, and when you have repeated the action a couple of times, lower the arm gently.

Massaging the elbow is not very difficult: support the arm at the elbow with one hand, and stroke around the elbow area with the other. Begin by making a circle all around the elbow, stroking smoothly; do not do this for too long, as relaxation rapidly turns to irritation if you do. Then use your thumb, with a counter-pressure from your fingers, or vice versa, to massage all over the outside of the elbow area. This is often very dry, and will benefit from much heavier oiling than usual. To finish, cradle the elbow in the palm of one hand and move the hand in a cradling, cupping motion around the point of the elbow.

Support your partner's wrist, and knead the fleshy part of the forearm with the heel of your hand; you can also pick up the muscles, if you wish. On the outer, bony side of the forearm, use your thumbs in a small kneading motion as shown. A forearm massage can be unexpectedly beneficial for anyone who drives long distances, as well as for anyone who has to work for any length of time at a keyboard, and it is very good for 'writer's cramp', especially when combined with a hand massage. Finish with the usual gentle effleurage strokes from the elbow down to the hand, and finally the fingers.

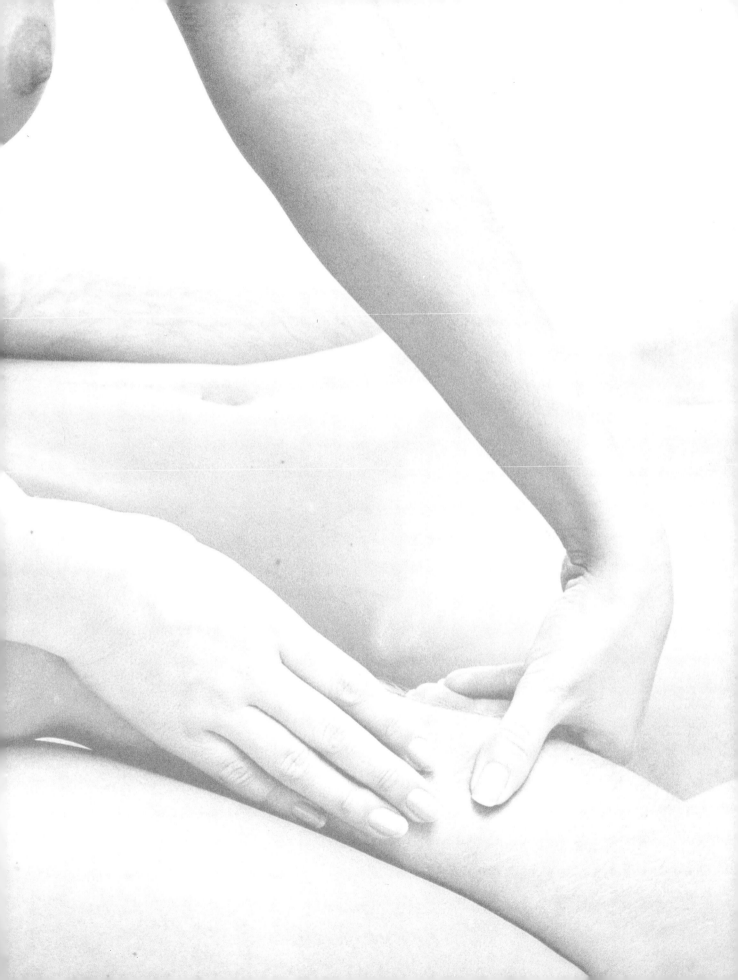

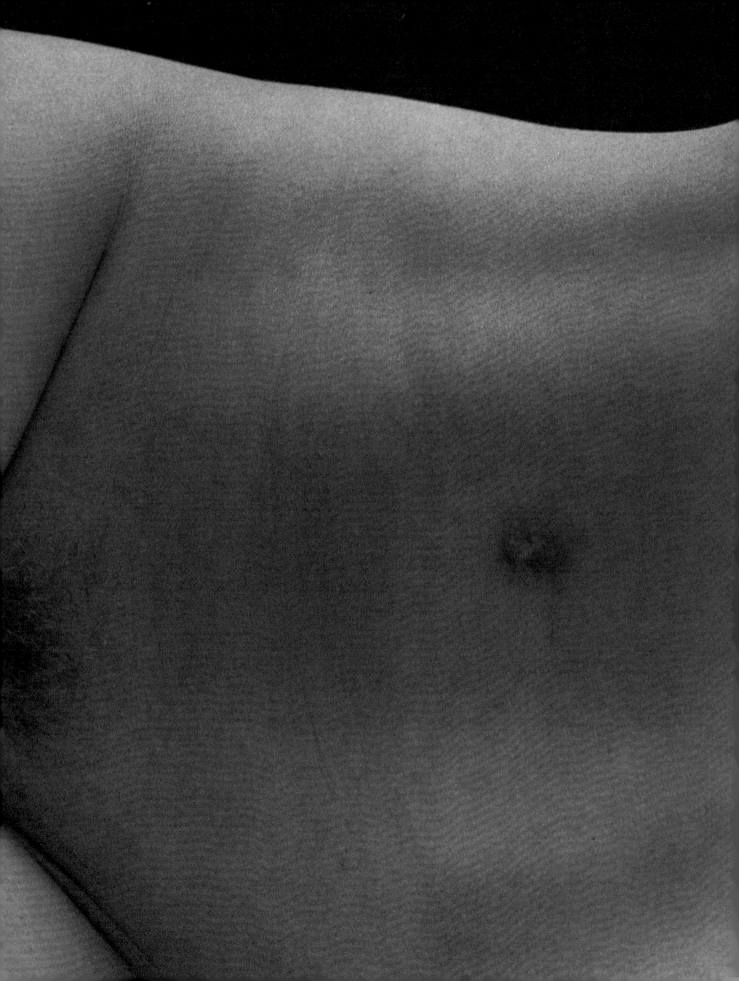

STOMACH

THE STOMACH, to be frank, is not much of an area for sensual massage — or to be accurate, most formal massage movements for the stomach are not very sensual. Also, because it is full of soft and rather delicate organs, it is not the sort of area that the inexperienced masseur or masseuse should set about with too much gusto.

On the other hand, the non-traditional and informal scope which the stomach offers for massage is considerable. From delicate brush-strokes with the fingertips, to kisses and nuzzling, or being brushed with long hair or a beard, there are all kinds of things which can make you wriggle with pleasure. 'Butterfly kisses' with the eyelashes; gently tracing a pattern with your tongue — but we do not need to elaborate. You can think of these things for yourself.

The stomach, like the back, provides an excellent area of smooth skin for massaging aromatherapy oils, and is (or can be) one of the most pleasurable areas for delicately massaging them in. Some aromatic essential oils are reputed to act as digestive tonics or stimulants, including cedarwood, chamomile, juniper, neroli and more — and of course, gentle massage is in itself an aid to digestion, provided you have not eaten too much.

However one simple technique which can relieve some stomach-aches is a double-handed stroke on the stomach. Place one hand on the lower stomach, with your fingers just below the navel, and place your other hand on top of it. Pressing quite hard at first, and moving your hands barely perceptibly, stroke upwards to the navel. When you reach it, release the pressure and return to the starting point with a gentle effleurage stroke. If it does not work quickly, or if it makes the pain worse, stop immediately; but you might be surprised at how often it does work. Never use this stroke (or any other form of abdominal massage) on a pregnant woman.

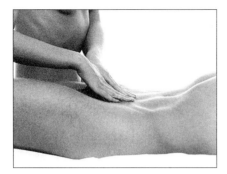

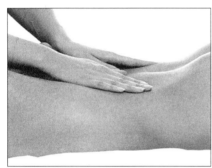

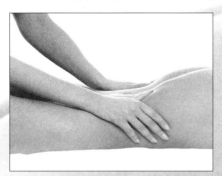

It is worth knowing how to do a basic abdominal massage, because although it is not immediately and obviously sensual, if it makes you feel better, you can go on to more enjoyable things. You carry out a simple effleurage sequence, and end with a back lift.

Begin with your fingertips just touching your partner's skin, rather over a hand-span below the navel. Taking care not to dig in, bring your hands down flat until they are in contact with the stomach, and move in a fan stroke upwards and outwards on either side of the navel. Continue the stroke over the top of the hips and around the waist, until your hands are under your partner's back and your fingers meet.

Allowing your hands to slip back around the waist towards the front of the body, lean backwards, maintaining enough pressure and tension to lift your partner's body slightly. When the heels of your hands meet at the front of your partner's body, repeat the movement towards the middle of their back, and again lift very gently. Repeat this once or twice more, then return your hands to their original starting position with an effleurage stroke. Be careful of your own back while you are doing this. Do not lean over too far, and remember to let your legs, rather than your back, take the strain. The whole sequence can be repeated twice.

Other possibilities for stomach massage include feather strokes, moving the hands clockwise; and placing your hands gently on your partner's stomach, lightly cupped. Feel the warmth gather under your hands; when it has built up, either flatten the hands or lift them up slightly. This is a little bit like a very slow, non-violent, non-percussive version of percussive cupping; in fact, it is about as unlike tapotement as it could be, while still maintaining a detectable resemblance.

BUTTOCKS

THE BUTTOCKS enjoy an unusual status in the canon of formal massage. While everyone agrees that buttock massages are enjoyable and beneficial, there is often some reluctance actually to do them. For once, Western society is not alone in this: many Eastern societies are even more puritanical about the buttocks.

In a sensual massage, this hindrance is converted into a positive advantage. While most of us are extremely choosy about whom we allow to touch our derrieres, partners in a loving relationship can display the degree of trust and intimacy which is required for a buttock massage.

It is important, however, not to assume that people will have the same feelings about their buttocks in an erotic context as they have in the context of a massage. People who are perfectly happy to do all sorts of things in bed with their partners may have a completely different reaction when their partner suggests a buttock massage. They may feel vulnerable, or simply uncomfortable.

It is a good idea, therefore, not to be too pushy about a buttock massage. If someone is unhappy, for whatever reason, fine: you don't have to insist. Instead, go for some other form of massage.

It is perfectly possible to do even a whole-body massage without paying very much attention to the buttocks; but equally, the experience of whole-body massages or of massages on other parts of the body may lead to a decline in the unwillingness to try a buttock massage as well.

From a purely rational viewpoint, most people today spend more time sitting down than they do walking about, and they spend all that time compressing their (largely unprotesting) buttocks. Because we do not usually suffer from buttock-ache with quite the same severity as we suffer from backache or stiff necks, it is all to easy to forget that the buttocks, too, can benefit from a relaxing, tension-relieving massage.

Apply the medium in the usual way. Then, beginning at the top of your partner's buttocks, lean over your partner with your hands either side of the spine, fingers overlapping, elbows outwards.

Move your hands down and around the sides of the buttocks, moulding the hands to the shape of your partner's body. Continue down to the base of the cheeks: at this point, your wrists should be almost touching, and your hands should be pointing outwards, at right angles to the legs and spine. The aim is to compress the two halves together, so that when you swing your hands upright again, you can do an easy, but very firm, effleurage stroke up over the top of the buttocks and return to the starting point.

Unusually, there are no light or superficial return strokes in a buttock massage: instead, there is a continuous firm or very firm pressure.

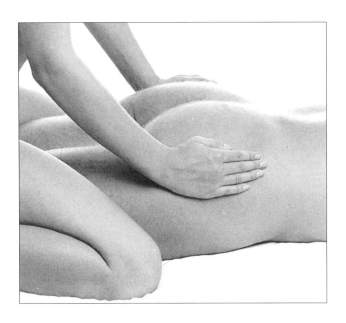

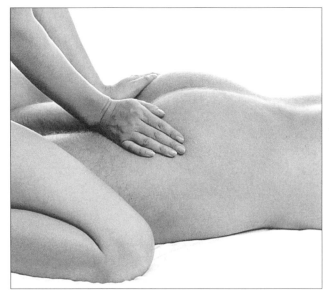

Other possibilities for buttock massage include deep, double-handed kneading using alternate strokes; reinforced kneading, using one hand on top of the other for extra pressure; wringing, to each side; all the usual tapotement strokes (cupping, beating, pounding and hacking — none of which, fortunately, is quite what it seems); and, as usual, light effleurage strokes to finish.

Another way to finish, favoured by most people, is a long, deep effleurage from the buttocks to the neck, usually done three times. Again, this would be finished with light effleurage strokes.

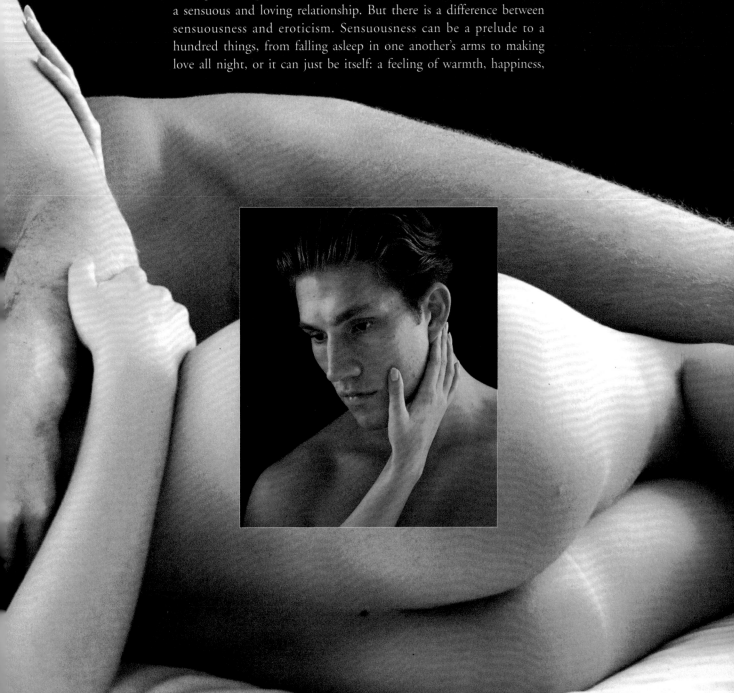

CHAPTER 7

Erotic
MASSAGE

A LOVER'S TOUCH can be a massage in itself. Like a good massage, it is simultaneously relaxing and invigorating. It conveys calm and excitement, reassurance and encouragement, rest and passion.

In the earlier part of the book, we have looked at conventional massage techniques; and as we have seen, these have their own place in a sensuous and loving relationship. But there is a difference between sensuousness and eroticism. Sensuousness can be a prelude to a hundred things, from falling asleep in one another's arms to making love all night, or it can just be itself: a feeling of warmth, happiness,

Nuzzling is a form of massage — with extra dimensions. There is the usual stimulating effect of being stroked; there is the warmth of the mouth, and of the breath; and there is an interchange of odours, including pheromones, which can be particularly stimulating to the person doing the nuzzling. It is also enormously comforting.

120

security, comfort, self-confidence. Eroticism is however inextricably associated with love-making, by its very definition.

At first sight, it might seem that 'erotic massage' is a contradiction in terms: after all, a massage is multi-dimensional, and can lead in many directions other than love-making, which is a very definite act. But when you think about it, a sexual relationship is also multi-dimensional, and some of those dimensions overlap with massage. There is a similar awareness of your own body and your partner's body; there is a similar concern with giving and receiving pleasure; and there is a similar emphasis on the primacy of touch.

By applying the lessons you have learnt in massage in an erotic context, you can improve both your love-making and your massage. Both are, after all, methods of non-verbal communication; and in both cases, what is communicated can often speak louder than words. Mutual awareness is one of the most important things. After all,

the bodies of men and women are different; a statement so obvious that even to mention it will raise a smile, and perhaps a cry of 'Vive la difference!' But the truth is, we often do forget this difference.

Most of us treat our partners' bodies as we would like our own to be treated; and to some extent, we treat their minds the same way. We imagine that what feels good to us, will feel good to them; we imagine that the order in which we do things, and the attention which we lavish on different parts of the body, are both as appropriate to them as they are to us.

This is not necessarily so; but because our partners want to please us, and because we want to please them, we may say nothing. There are times when this is appropriate, because there are things which may be very important to one party, but not the other. There are other times though when the only result is a misunderstanding: one partner is doing something for no other reason than that he or she mistakenly believes the other person enjoys it.

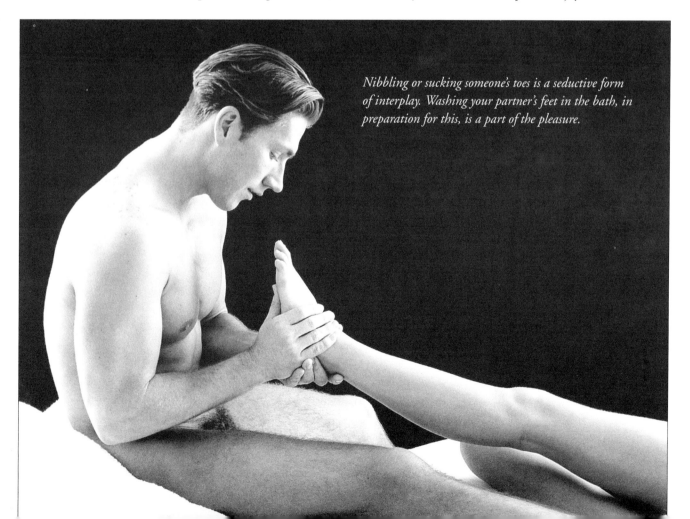

Nibbling or sucking someone's toes is a seductive form of interplay. Washing your partner's feet in the bath, in preparation for this, is a part of the pleasure.

Communicating such preferences is not a matter for words, unless it is something you really do not like; after all, when you are trying to please someone, the last thing you want to hear is 'Don't do that!' No: the answer is to respond more enthusiastically to the positive, and less enthusiastically to what you do not enjoy. Erotic massage is the perfect medium for this. Unlike ordinary massage, where you are to a greater or lesser extent following a series of pre-planned moves, erotic massage is much more a matter of response and reaction; and unlike ordinary foreplay, which can often follow an increasingly familiar pattern, it actively encourages exploration, playfulness, and a rediscovery of one another's bodies.

In an erotic massage, almost all communication is non-verbal. Often, it is incredibly subtle, too: the tiniest shift in weight, or a barely perceptible change in tension or relaxation of a muscle, even the flicker of an eyelid. All of

these can be signals from your partner to continue, or stop, or change emphasis. More obvious signals can include sighs and moans, or a particular sparkle in the eye, or even taking your partner's hand and placing it where you want to be touched.

Another difference between an erotic massage and a sensual massage is that you can use far more of your body. The lips and the mouth are obviously sensual: as the poet Catullus wrote in the first century BC 'Give me a thousand kisses, then a hundred, then a second thousand, then a second hundred…' But there is more to the mouth than kissing: there is licking, and nuzzling, and sucking and even gentle biting. Graze your cheek along your partner's skin; feel the soft skin of their shoulder on the soft skin under your own chin.

Examples could be elaborated infinitely. Some men like to be brushed with their lovers' breasts. Toes have their erotic adherents. Ear-lobes can be kissed, nibbled, caressed.

'Whole-body massage' can mean many things. Sitting back to back, and resting your head first on one of your partner's shoulders, and then on the other (they do the same to you) reminds you what a neglected sensual area the back normally is, while lying full length on your partner and massaging them with the whole of your body can be strangely, and unexpectedly, relaxing. Another possibility is to share a shower, soaping one another all over, and then trying to wash your partner all over without excessive use of the hands.

The backs of the knees are a sensuous zone for many, and, of course, the more conventionally erogenous zones such as the insides of the thighs can be given much more attention then they would normally receive even in a sensual massage. The term 'whole-body massage' takes on a new meaning when it is given not just *to* the whole body, but also *with* the whole body. But to catalogue such charms and delights is pointless; what you and your partner need to do together is to explore the ones which please you both, both in giving and receiving.

It would be foolish, too, to pretend that there are universal male preferences and universal female preferences. What one person finds delightful, another may find distasteful or merely uninteresting. Some people love to have their nipples kissed; others find it actively uncomfortable. Old fears can be reawakened, or old fantasies reinvigorated, by one and the same act: spanking would be a classic example.

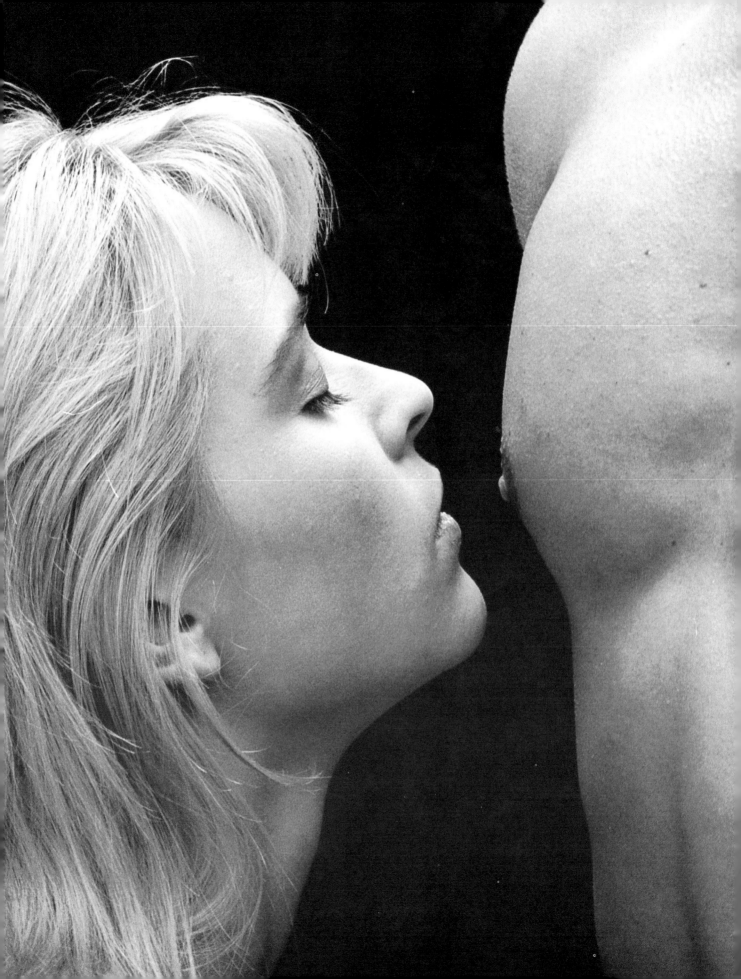

If you are fully aware of one another's responses, such differences in personal desires will hardly even be noticeable; the slightest signal will suffice, and you will quite naturally either intensify your response, or stop. Admittedly, there may be variations in what each person wants from one day to another, and it is possible to misread signals; so even if you thought you detected a negative response to something on one occasion, you might still try it another time.

To sum up, an erotic massage enables you to start every love-making session afresh, removing old inhibitions and fears, and rediscover your partner's body anew; but at the same time, it allows you to build on what you already know and love about one another; and you really cannot ask for much more than that.

INDEX